California
Science

Science Content Support
Grade 5

Teacher Edition

Harcourt
SCHOOL PUBLISHERS

Visit *The Learning Site!*
www.harcourtschool.com

ISBN-13: 978-0-15-352290-1
ISBN-10: 0-15-352290-9

8 9 10 0607 20 19 18 17
4500671419

Contents

Getting Ready for Science

Unit 1 • Elements and Compounds

Unit 2 • Structures of Living Things

Unit 5 • **The Solar System**

Vocabulary

Name _____

Date _____

Lesson 1—What Tools Do Scientists Use?

A. Explore Word Meanings

Match the clue on the left with the term on the right.

c	the amount of matter in an object	**a.** forceps
d	a measure of gravity's pull	**b.** balance
a	a tool used to pick up or hold small objects	**c.** mass
f	a tool used to measure the length and width of objects	**d.** weight
g	a tool used to measure forces, such as weight or friction	**e.** microscope
h	a tool used to measure the volume of a liquid	**f.** ruler
e	a tool that makes small objects appear larger	**g.** spring scale
i	how much space something takes up	**h.** graduated cylinder
b	a tool that measures the amount of matter in an object	**i.** volume

B. Suffixes

The suffix –ative means "of, relating to." Use this information to draw a line between each word and its definition.

qualitative observation   observations relating to the quantity, or amount, of something

quantitative observation   observations relating to the quality or kind of something

Study Skills

Name _____

Date _____

Lesson 1—What Tools Do Scientists Use?

Connect Ideas

Graphic organizers are drawings that help you organize information. They can help you connect ideas.

- One kind of organizer is a bubble map. On a bubble map, the main idea is written in the center bubble. The ideas that are related to the main idea are written in the surrounding bubbles.

Complete the bubble map with the tools you would use to make observations. Possible answers shown.

© Harcourt

Name _____

Date _____

Lesson 1—What Tools Do Scientists Use?

1. Investigation Skill Practice—Measure

Draw a line to connect each qualitative observation with the necessary tool.

the length and width of a book   graduated cylinder

the mass of your shoe   spring scale

the weight of your pet dog   pan balance

the volume of water in a container   ruler

2. Reading Focus Skill Practice—Main Idea and Details

Read the selection. Underline the main idea. List at least two details about the main idea. Possible answers shown.

Do you wear glasses? Did you know that people have been wearing glasses for hundreds of years? Eyeglasses, or spectacles, have been around since the thirteenth century. The first pair of wearable glasses that we know of was invented in Italy by Salvino D'Armate. The year was 1284! In 1752, James Ayscough invented glasses that had green or blue lenses. He thought that the light from clear lenses was hard on the eyes. They were a little bit like our modern sunglasses!

Eyeglasses, or spectacles, have been around since the thirteenth century. The first pair of wearable glasses was invented by Salvino D'Armate.

© Harcourt

Name _____

Date _____

Lesson 2—What Inquiry Skills Do Scientists Use?

A. Explore Word Meanings

For each sentence, fill in the blank with a word or words from the box that best completes the sentence.

investigation	inquiry	experiment	dependent variable	control variable

1. The thing that is being controlled or measured in an investigation is called the <u>dependent variable</u>

2. An organized way to gather information so you can answer questions is called an <u>inquiry</u>

3. An <u>investigation</u> is a procedure that is carried out to gather data about an object or an event.

4. A procedure you carry out under controlled conditions to test a hypothesis is an <u>experiment</u>

5. A <u>control variable</u> is the part of an investigation that remains the same so the dependent variable can be measured.

A. Explore Word Meanings

Draw a line to match the term on the left with the clue on the right.

observe   use data to draw conclusions about things you haven't directly observed

predict   decide how two things are the same

compare   group or organize objects or events into categories

classify   use observations and data to form an idea of what will happen

infer   use your senses to gather information about objects and events

---

Name _____

Science Concepts

3. **Circle the word or words in each sentence that make the sentence true.**

   a. Scientists use microscopes to make (quantitative/qualitative) observations, which do not involve measurements or numbers.

   b. Thermometers and spring scales are tools that help scientists make (quantitative/qualitative) observations.

   c. A (microscope/thermometer) lets you see details that you could not see with your eyes alone.

   d. A curved glass can (disappear/magnify) objects, or make them look larger.

   e. Anton van Leeuwenhouk used a lens to see creatures in a drop of water. He called them (animalcules/molecules).

   f. The main parts of a microscope include the (earpiece/eyepiece), stage, base, nosepiece, and adjustment knobs.

   g. Galileio Galilei made the first (thermometer/microscope) in 1592.

   h. Fahrenheit made a thermometer using (mercury/hydrogen) in a sealed glass tube and marked units called degrees on the tube.

   i. The Celsius scale has (100/1000) degrees between the freezing point of water and the boiling point of water.

4. **Draw a line to connect tool on the left with the unit of measure on the right.**

   spring scale   grams or kilograms

   balance   centimeters and millimeters

   graduated cylinder   newtons

   ruler   milliliters or liters

Right page (Lesson Quick Study)

Name _____

Date _____

Getting Ready for Science, Lesson 2

Lesson 2—What Inquiry Skills Do Scientists Use?

1. Investigation Skill Practice–Develop a Testable Question

Suppose you want to find out how sunlight affects rose bushes. You want to perform an experiment in which rose bushes are exposed to various amounts of sunlight. Which of the following questions is a testable question for this experiment?

1. How do rose bushes use sunlight to grow?

2. Why do rose bushes grow better in more light?

3. How do different amounts of sunlight affect rose bushes?

2. Reading Focus Skill Practice–Main Idea and Details

Read the selection. Underline the main idea. Write two details that support the main idea.

Even though you may not notice, you are using inquiry skills all the time. When you walk in your house and smell food cooking, you use your senses to observe and draw conclusions about what is for dinner based on that information. When you put away clean clothes, you may classify them—sort them into groups of shirts, pants, and socks. You may compare one batter's swing with another batter's swing at a baseball game. How many other inquiry skills do you use every day?

Possible answer: You can observe the smell of food cooking and draw

conclusions about what it is. You classify clothing when you it sort it

by type. _____

_____

© Harcourt

Use with Getting Ready for Science.   (page 1 of 2)   Science Content Support   CS 7

Left page (Study Skills)

Name _____

Date _____

Getting Ready for Science, Lesson 2

Lesson 2—What Inquiry Skills Do Scientists Use?

Pose Questions

Asking questions as you read can help you understand what you are learning.

- Form questions as you read. Think about how ideas and events are related.
- Use the questions to guide your reading. Look for the answers as you read.

Complete the chart with your own questions about what you read. Then, answer the questions with information you find in the lesson.
Possible answers shown.

What Inquiry Skills Do Scientists Use?	
Questions	Answers
1. How is inquiry different from asking questions about something?	Inquiry is an organized way of getting information. You can be curious about something without trying to get information to answer your questions.
2. What do you do with the data after you've collected it?	You interpret the data and draw conclusions based on what questions you want to answer.
3. What is a testable question?	A question you can answer by conducting an investigation.
4. Why do you need a control variable in an investigation?	You need one part of the investigation to remain the same so you can measure the dependent variable.
5. How is an investigation different from an experiment?	An experiment has more steps than an investigation. You carry out an experiment under controlled conditions to test a hypothesis.

© Harcourt

CS 6   Science Content Support   Use with Getting Ready for Science.

© Harcourt

Name _____

Science Concepts

3. Check (✓) the statements below that agree with the information found in the lesson.

✓ You can use your senses to gather information about objects and events.

___ You should never ask questions about an object or event.

✓ Inquiry skills are skills that help you answer questions about an object or event.

✓ If you study an object and diagrams of the object, you are observing the object.

___ If you compare two objects, you group them into categories based on certain characteristics.

✓ When you infer, you use logical reasoning to come to a conclusion based on data and observations.

✓ The first step in an investigation is to develop a testable question.

___ The control variable in an investigation is the variable being measured.

4. Circle the word that best completes each sentence.

A. You can use your _____ from an experiment to draw conclusions.

Predictions   (data)   hypothesis

B. You can use a _____ to test something before building the real thing.

(model)   inquiry   conclusion

C. You can use tables, reports, and diagrams to _____ the results of your experiment to others.

predict   (communicate)   hypothesize

D. When you _____, you suggest an outcome or explanation that can be tested in an experiment.

inquire   communicate   (hypothesize)

CS 8   Science Content Support (page 2 of 2) **Use with Getting Ready for Science.**

Extra
Support

Name _____

Date _____

Getting Ready for Science, Lesson 2

Lesson 2—What Inquiry Skills Do Scientists Use?

Identifying Variables

A scientist wanted to determine whether the color of a house's roof would affect how much heat the house would absorb. The scientist decided to perform an experiment to test this idea. She set up six identical birdhouses together in a field and put thermometers inside each birdhouse to record the temperature during the day. Three of the birdhouses had black roofs, and three of the birdhouses had white roofs. She recorded the temperatures of each birdhouse at 9 am, noon, and 3 pm each day for a week.

1. Which variable or variables in the experiment did the scientist change?
   The color of the birdhouse roof.

2. Which variable or variables in the experiment did the scientist keep the same?
   The type and size of birdhouse, the time of day temperatures were recorded, the placement of the birdhouses.

3. What was the dependent variable that was being measured in the experiment?
   The temperatures of the different birdhouses.

4. Which question above describes the control variable?
   The things that stayed the same; list from question #2.

© Harcourt

Use with Getting Ready for Science.   (page 1 of 2)   Science Content Support   CS 9

Science Content Support   CS 8–CS 9

Name _____

Vocabulary Power

Getting Ready for Science, Lesson 3

Name _____

Date _____

Lesson 3—How Do Scientists Record and Interpret Data?

A. Explore Word Meanings

Draw a line to match the clue on the left to the term on the right.

a sketch or other visual representation that shows an idea or object — criteria

putting objects into groups based on your criteria — classify

specific qualities you use to put objects into groups — conclusion

a decision you make based on information — diagram

B. Graphs and Diagrams

Complete the table with information you can illustrate using different types of graphs and diagrams.

Type of graph or diagram	Uses
bar graph	used to compare information about different objects, events, or groups
line graph	used to show how things change over a period of time
circle graph	used to show parts of a whole
diagram	used to show the parts of something

© Harcourt

Use with Getting Ready for Science.   Science Content Support   CS 11

Name _____

A scientist has developed a new type of fertilizer for lawns. The scientist hypothesizes that using the fertilizer will lead to lawns with greener, thicker grass. The scientist wants to run an experiment that will test whether the new fertilizer is more effective than a traditional lawn fertilizer.

Use the information above to answer the questions below.

1. In the experiment, name some variables that the scientist will want to keep the same.

   Answers will vary. Some examples include the amount of fertilizer added, the amount of water and sunlight the grass receives, the location of the areas used, and the type of grass used for each sample.

2. Describe the variable that the scientist will change and how the variable will be changed in the experiment.

   The scientist will change the type of fertilizer that is added to the grass. Some grass will receive the traditional fertilizer, while other grass will receive the new fertilizer.

3. Explain what things the scientist might use as a dependent variable, or the variable that would be measured as part of the experiment.

   Some examples include the color of the grass, the height of the grass, and the thickness of the grass.

4. Describe some results that would support the scientist's hypothesis.

   The grass that receives the new fertilizer is greener and thicker than the grass that receives the traditional fertilizer.

© Harcourt

Name _____

Date _____

Lesson 3—How Do Scientists Record and Interpret Data?

Organize Information

A graphic organizer can help you make sense of the facts you read.
- Tables, charts, and webs are graphic organizers that can show main ideas and important details.
- A graphic organizer can help you classify and categorize information. It can also help you understand the relationship between the subject of the chapter and each lesson.

Complete the graphic organizer with details about ways that scientists record and interpret data. Possible answers shown.

```
                    Ways Scientists Record
                     and Interpret Data
        ┌──────────────────┼──────────────────┐
```

Tables and Charts
- a good way to organize data so that you can understand and interpret it
- tables can help you see patterns in your data
- tables can also help you draw conclusions

Graphs
- bar graphs help you compare information
- line graphs help you show changes that happen over time
- circle graphs can help you show parts of a whole

Diagrams
- a drawing or sketch of an idea or object
- can help make complex things easier to understand
- can show the inside parts of something

Name _____

Date _____

Lesson 3—How Do Scientists Record and Interpret Data?

1. **Investigation Skill Practice–Record Data**

Suzanne collected information about the temperature at noon in her town each day for a week. Sunday it was 24°C and sunny. Monday it was 23°C and sunny. Tuesday it rained and the temperature fell to 16°C. Wednesday it rained and was 19°C. The next three days were sunny and were 20°C, 23°C, and 23°C, in that order. Complete the table using the data Suzanne collected.

Day	Temperature	Rain or Sun?
Sunday	24°C	sun
Monday	23°C	sun
Tuesday	16°C	rain
Wednesday	19°C	rain
Thursday	20°C	sun
Friday	23°C	sun
Saturday	23°C	sun

2. **Reading Skill Practice–Main Idea and Details**

Circle the details that support the main idea.

Main Idea: Tables and charts can help you draw conclusions from your data.

1. Tables and charts are good ways to organize data.

2. Tables and charts make it harder to interpret data.

3. You can record information in a table as you collect it.

4. Tables and charts make it easier to see patterns in your data.

5. A bar graph can be used to display and compare data.

Name _____
Date _____

Lesson 3—How Do Scientists Record and Interpret Data?

Recording/Interpreting Data

A. Several scientists worked throughout a state to count the populations of four different types of birds at three different locations in the state. They organized the data in a table, which is shown below. Use the data table to answer the questions.

	Robin	Wren	Sparrow	Cardinal
Location #1	243	112	355	210
Location #2	56	45	250	199
Location #3	178	87	289	156

1. Create a row that shows the total number of each bird observed in the state.
Robin-477; Wren-244; Sparrow-894; Cardinal-565

2. Which bird was present in the greatest numbers?
Sparrow

3. Which bird had the lowest population in the state?
Wren

4. Create a graph that shows the total populations of each type of bird.
Answers will vary, but should list all four birds and their total population in the state.

Use with Getting Ready for Science.   Science Content Support   CS 15

Name _____

Science Concepts

3. Decide which word completes each sentence. Write the letter in the blank.

b When you _____ objects, you group them by specific qualities.   **a.** criteria

a If you group single-engine planes together and twin-engine planes together, you are using the number of engines as your _____.   **b.** classify

d Tables and charts are both ways to _____ data so that you can understand and interpret it.   **c.** conclusion

e As you _____ data during an investigation, you can write it in a table.   **d.** organize

c You use the information you collect during an investigation to draw a _____.   **e.** collect

4. Use the words in the box to complete each sentence.

bar graph	diagram	patterns	whole

a. Both a table and a bar graph can be used to compare information about objects, groups, or events.

b. Looking for patterns in your data can help you draw conclusions.

c. A circle graph can show the parts of a whole .

d. You can use a diagram to show the inside parts of a submarine and how the parts work together.

CS 14 Science Content Support (page 2 of 2) Use with Getting Ready for Science.

Name _____

B. A student found the chart shown below. It shows some of the volcanoes that have erupted in western United States.

Volcanic Eruptions

Ranier
St. Helens
Shasta
Lassen

4000   2000
Years Ago

1. How long ago was the first volcanic eruption
About 3000 years

2. Which volcano has erupted the most times?
St. Helens

3. Which eruption was most recent?
St. Helens

4. Make a bar graph showing the number of eruptions of each of the volcanoes. Arrange the graph to show the number of eruptions from least to most.

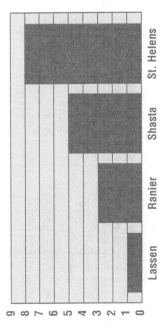

9
8
7
6
5
4
3
2
1
0
Lassen   Ranier   Shasta   St. Helens

Name _____

C. The following chart shows the numbers of gas and oil wells in four counties of California. The data also shows the amount of gas and oil produced from each.

Country	Number of Oil Wells	Number of Gas Wells	Barrels of Oil produced	Gas produced (mcf)	Total Number of wells
Fresno	1,966	6	7,218,816	2,575,047	1,972
Kern	36,955	142	196,774,148	209,394,641	37,097
Los Angeles	3,189	5	27,608,872	11,921,115	3,194
Ventura	1,839	7	8,508,570	6,389,527	1,846
Totals	43,949	160	240,110,406	230,280,330	44,109

1. Fill in the column that shows the total number of wells by adding the number of oil wells plus the number of gas wells. Fill in the row to show the total numbers of wells and production. (You may use a calculator to help you.)

2. What can you conclude about the number of units of gas (mcf) produced per well as compared to the total number of units of oil (barrels) produced per well? **The number of units of gas is almost equal to the number of units of oil produced. Since there are fewer gas wells than oil wells, the units of gas per well must be greater than the units of oil per well.**

3. Show the number of oil wells found in these four counties in a pie graph. Color Fresno County in blue, Kern County in red, Los Angeles County in yellow, and Ventura County in green.

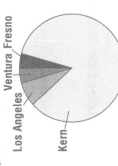

Los Angeles   Ventura Fresno

Kern

Name _____

Date _____

Lesson 4—What Is the Scientific Method?

A. Explore Word Meanings

Match the clue on the left to the term on the right. Write the letter in the blank.

__c__ a series of steps used to plan and carry out investigations   a. report

__b__ the information you gather during an investigation   b. evidence

__d__ a possible answer to a question, which can be tested   c. scientific method

__a__ a written account of the findings of your investigation   d. hypothesis

B. Sequence

Use the numbers 1 through 5 to put the steps of the scientific method in the correct order.

__3__ Plan an investigation

__5__ Draw conclusions and write a report

__2__ Form a hypothesis

__4__ Conduct the investigation

__1__ Observe and ask questions

© Harcourt

Use with Getting Ready for Science.

Science Content Support   **CS 19**

Name _____

D. There are eight National Parks in the state of California. The total number of acres and the number of acres owned by the federal government in each park is shown below. Use this data table to answer the questions.

Park Name	Total Acres	Federal Acres	Nonfederal Acres
Channel Islands	249,353	70,519	178,834
Death Valley	3,367,628	3,348,929	18,699
Joshua Tree	1,022,976	782,829	240,147
Kings Canyon	461,901	461,845	56
Lassen Volcanic	106,372	106,366	6
Redwood	105,516	71,715	33,801
Sequoia	402,510	402,334	176
Yosemite	761,266	759,530	1,736
	6,228,169	5,933,548	294,621

1. Fill in the column at the right that shows the number of nonfederal acres in each park.

2. Which park has the smallest number of nonfederal acres?
   Lassen Volcanic

3. Make a bar graph that shows the parks from smallest to largest.

National Parks

© Harcourt

CS 18   Science Content Support (page 4 of 4) Use with Getting Ready for Science.

Name _____

Date _____

Getting Ready for Science, Lesson 4

Lesson 4—What Is the Scientific Method?

1. Investigation Skill Practice–Draw Conclusions

Suppose you fill two saucers with water. You set one outside on a warm, sunny day and one in a shady spot. After one day, the saucer in the sunny spot is empty. The saucer in the shade still has water in it. What conclusions can you draw from this information? **Possible answer shown.**

Possible answer: The direct sunlight caused the water in the saucer to

evaporate more quickly.

_____

2. Reading Skill Practice–Main Idea and Details

Read the selection. Underline the main idea. List at least two details.

A good scientist always writes a report about his or her investigation, even when the results do not support the hypothesis. At first, the idea that you should tell everyone your hypothesis was wrong might seem strange. What do scientists do if the evidence from their experiment does not support their hypothesis? They write a report about the investigation. They can use details from the report to repeat the experiment. This way, they make sure the result wasn't just a mistake. Then they, or other scientists, can use the data from the investigation to form a new hypothesis and plan more investigations.

A scientist can use the report to do the experiment again to make sure

the result wasn't just a mistake. They, or other scientists, can use the

data from the report to form a new hypothesis.

© Harcourt

Use with Getting Ready for Science. (page 1 of 2) Science Content Support

---

Name _____

Date _____

Getting Ready for Science, Lesson 4

Lesson 4—What Is the Scientific Method?

Use an Anticipation Guide

An anticipation guide can help you anticipate, or predict, what you will learn as you read.

Complete the anticipation guide using information from the lesson.

Observe, and Ask Questions		
Reading Check	Prediction	Correct?
What can help you form a testable question?	your observations and other experiments	yes
Form a Hypothesis		
Reading Check	Prediction	Correct?
What does a hypothesis do?		
Plan an Investigation		
Reading Check	Prediction	Correct?
What steps go into planning an investigation?		
Conduct an Investigation		
Reading Check	Prediction	Correct?
What is done during an investigation?		
Draw Conclusions		
Reading Check	Prediction	Correct?
How do tables, graphs, and charts help you draw conclusions?		
Write a Report		
Reading Check	Prediction	Correct?
Why is it important to write a report?	Predictions should show thoughtful reflection.	Students should evaluate using information in the lesson.

© Harcourt

Science Content Support Use with Getting Ready for Science.

Science Content Support

Lesson 4—What Is the Scientific Method?

Applying Scientific Method

A. A scientist decided to do an investigation on which trees lose their leaves earliest in the fall. Below is a list of steps in the investigation. Number the steps in the correct order so that the investigation is following the scientific method.

Step __5__ The scientist analyzed data. The data showed that the elm tree had lost its leaves by October 16th, the oak tree has lost its leaves by November 10th, and the maple tree had lost its leaves by November 25th.

Step __2__ The scientist hypothesized that the maple tree would be the last tree to lose its leaves in the fall.

Step __4__ The scientist observed all the trees in the area during the fall. He wrote down the day each type of tree had finally lost all its leaves.

Step __1__ The scientist looked around at the trees in the area. He noticed that some trees seemed to lose their leaves early in the fall, while others still had them late in the season. He wondered if certain types of trees lost their leaves earlier than others.

Step __3__ The scientist decided to observe all the trees in his area and record the dates in which different types of trees lost their leaves.

Step __6__ The scientist wrote a report, describing the steps of the investigation, the data he collected, and his conclusion.

B. Fill in the blanks below with some of the steps you would use to investigate whether using high-octane gasoline in a car would improve gas mileage. Make sure you describe the steps in the order they would occur.

Step 1 Your uncle drives his car to work every day for a year. During the year, he sometimes fills it with regular gasoline, and sometimes with premium-grade gasoline. It seems like it gets better gas mileage when he uses the premium-grade gasoline, but he isn't quite sure. You wonders if the premium-grade gasoline really does give better gas mileage.

© Harcourt

Science Concepts

3. **Circle the letter of the best answer to each question.**

1. What is the scientific method?
   - **A. A series of steps scientists use to plan and carry out investigations.**
   - B. Inquiry skills that you use in planning an experiment.

2. What do all investigations start with?
   - A. an experiment
   - **B. a testable question**

3. What is the second step in the scientific method?
   - A. Perform an experiment.
   - **B. Form a hypothesis.**

4. How could you test a hypothesis that a round-balloon rocket will travel a shorter distance than a long-balloon rocket?
   - **A. Conduct an investigation.**
   - B. Do research at the library.

5. What do you need to do before you conduct an investigation?
   - **A. Plan the investigation.**
   - B. Observe another person's investigation.

4. **Choose the word that completes each sentence.**

6. The results of an investigation will either (**support**/disprove) your hypothesis or fail to support it.

7. You must be able to (support/**test**) your hypothesis.

8. When you conduct an investigation, it is important to observe, measure, and (**record**/prove) everything that happens.

9. Identifying (**patterns**/problems) in your data can help you draw conclusions.

10. Writing a report about how you conducted your investigation and what the results were is a way to (observe/**communicate**).

© Harcourt

Lesson 1– What Are Atoms and Elements?

A. Word Families

Choose a word or words from the box that belongs to the same word family.

atom	element	periodic table	molecule	mixture

1. atomic _____ atom

2. elementary _____ element

3. periodically _____ periodic table

4. molecular _____ molecule

5. mix _____ mixture

B. Context Clues

Choose a word or words from the box to complete each sentence.

compound	periodic table	physical properties	molecule	element

1. When a substance is made of two or more different elements, it is called a(n) _____ compound _____ .

2. To help them remember the properties of each element, scientists refer to the _____ periodic table _____ .

3. Color, shape, melting point, and freezing point are all _____ physical properties _____ of a substance.

4. Two or more atoms that are joined together are called a(n) _____ molecule _____ .

5. A substance made of only one kind of atom is a(n) _____ element _____ .

Step 2 You form a hypothesis. You hypothesize that his car will get better gas mileage when it uses premium gasoline.

_____

_____

Step 3 You plan an investigation. You decide to record the gas mileage when his car uses regular gasoline for one month. You then will record the gas mileage when his car uses premium gasoline for one month.

_____

_____

Step 4 You conduct the investigation. For one month your uncle uses regular gasoline and for one month he uses premium gasoline. You record the mileage each time.

_____

_____

Step 5 You collect the data and use it to create an average gas mileage chart. The chart is shown below.

	Mileage
Regular Gas	22.5
Premium Gas	22.5

Step 6 You conclude that your uncle's car does not get better gas mileage with premium gas than with regular gas and that your hypothesis was not supported by the investigation. You write a report, including your procedure, data, analysis, and conclusion.

_____

_____

Name _____
Date _____

Lesson 1– What Are Atoms and Elements?

Use a K-W-L Chart

A K-W-L chart can help you focus on what you already know about a topic and what you want to learn about it

- Use the K column to list what you already know about atoms and elements.
- Use the W column to list what you want to learn about atoms and elements.
- Use the L column to list what you have learned about the topic from your reading.

Complete the K-W-L chart as you read this lesson.

Atoms and Elements		
What I Know	**What I Want to Learn**	**What I Learned**
• I know that an atom is the smallest part of a substance.	• Why is it called an atom?	• Statements should contain accurate information from the lesson.
• Statements should reflect students' common knowledge.	• Questions should show thoughtful reflection. Some questions may not be answered in the lesson.	•
•	•	•

Name _____
Date _____

Lesson 1– What Are Atoms and Elements?

1. Investigation Skill Practice–Classify

An element contains one kind of atom. A compound is made of atoms of two or more elements. Look at the list below. Classify each item as an element or a compound.

hydrogen	salt	carbon
methane	nitrogen	propane
carbon dioxide	oxygen	water

Elements
hydrogen
carbon
nitrogen
oxygen

Compounds
salt
methane
propane
carbon dioxide
water

2. Reading Skill Practice–Main Idea and Details

Read the selection. Underline the main idea. Write 2 details on the lines below.

There are important pieces of information you can gather from the periodic table of the elements. You can tell if an element is metal or nonmetal. The metals are on the left. The nonmetals are on the right. You can also tell the element's symbol, name, atomic mass, and atomic number. These are useful for decoding the chemical name of a molecule.

Details: You can tell if an element is metal, or nonmetal; and its symbol, name, atomic mass, and atomic number.

_____

_____

Name _____

Date _____

Lesson 1– What Are Atoms and Elements?

The Periodic Table

A. History of the Periodic Table

In the past, many chemists tried to organize the elements in a sensible way. They tried many different ways, but found best success when Dmitri Mendeleev created the Periodic Table of the Elements.

Imagine that you are a chemist living in the early 1900s. You know the properties of the following 10 elements. Experiment with different ways to organize the elements into a chart. Discuss your ideas with others.

beryllium	solid	4 protons	gray	combines easily with oxygen	high melting point
boron	solid	5 protons	black or dark brown	combines with nitrogen	poor electrical conductor
carbon	solid	6 protons	varies with form	combines with itself	comes in graphite, diamond, and amorphous forms
helium	gas	2 protons	colorless	can combine with oxygen	low melting point
hydrogen	gas	1 protons	colorless	combines with oxygen, fluorine, chlorine	most common element in universe
fluorine	gas	9 protons	yellow	highly reactive with all elements	very corrosive
lithium	solid	3 protons	silvery	combines with oxygen, nitrogen, carbon, and hydrogen	low density
neon	gas	10 protons	varies	rarely combines with other elements, except fluorine	emits colors with electrical charge
nitrogen	gas	7 protons	colorless	combines with boron, hydrogen, and itself	most abundant gas in atmosphere
oxygen	gas	8 protons	colorless	combines with nearly all other elements including itself	poor conductor of heat and electricity

Use with Unit 1.   (page 1 of 4)   Science Content Support

© Harcourt

Name _____

3. Read the Periodic Table

Consider the compound for table salt: NaCl. Use the periodic table in your textbook to answer the following questions.

What elements make up table salt?
sodium and chlorine

How many atoms of each element are in table salt?
one of sodium and one of chlorine

4. Physical Properties

Use the words listed in the box to describe the physical properties of each substance. Then add your own descriptions of physical properties for each substance.

sticky	liquid at room temperature
colorless	able to dissolve in water
odorless	solid at room temperature
lumpy	hard

A. water
liquid at room temperature; odorless; colorless; Students should add additional descriptions.

B. peanut butter
sticky; solid at room temperature; Students should add additional descriptions.

C. cardboard
hard, solid at room temperature; Students should add additional descriptions.

D. window glass
hard, colorless, solid at room temperature; Students should add additional descriptions.

Science Content Support   (page 2 of 2)   Use with Unit 1.

© Harcourt

Science Content Support   CS 28–CS 29

Element Cards (page 3 of 4)

H	Chlorine	Argon	O
Al	Helium	N	Oxygen
Nitrogen	Ar	Carbon	Na
He	Calcium	Cl	Aluminum
Sodium	C	Ca	Hydrogen

Use with Unit 1.   Science Content Support   CS 31

B. Using the Periodic Table

The Periodic Table we use today organizes the elements by atomic number. One reason it works so well is that the elements in each column have similar properties.

Periodic Table

Each box tells the atomic number, name, and symbol of an element. The symbols come from the English, Latin, or other name for the element.

1. What is the atomic number for oxygen? __8__

2. What does this number mean? __the number of protons in the atom__

C. Learn some element symbols with the concentration game on the next page.

- Copy and cut out the cards or copy them onto index cards.
- Shuffle and place them face down in a grid.
- You and a partner take turns flipping over two cards. Keep the cards if you match an element name and symbol. If not, turn the cards over.
- Play until all the cards are matched. Shuffle and play again.

CS 30   Science Content Support   (page 2 of 4)   Use with Unit 1.

Name _____

SKINNER
GET
SCHEDULE

C. The Periodic Table shows patterns in the elements. Elements in the same column have similar properties. Answer the questions below.

1. How does atomic number change across a row? Down a column?

   It increases.

2. Where are the metals located in the Periodic Table? Where are the nonmetals and semimetals located?

   Metals are located on the left side. The nonmetals and semimetals are located on the right side.

3. Argon and xenon are gases. They do not combine easily with other elements. Identify another element with similar properties. Explain your answer.

   Students should identify any element in column 18 and explain that elements in the same column have similar properties.

4. Hydrogen and sodium combine easily with chlorine. Identify another element that combines easily with chlorine and explain your answer.

   Students should identify any element in column 1 and explain that elements in the same column have similar properties.

5. If you put lithium in water, not much happens. Add sodium to water and you will see a small amount of bubbling. Potassium and water make an explosive combination. Describe the pattern seen in column 1. Predict what might happen if you mix water and rubidium.

   The elements become more reactive as you go down the column.
   Rubidium is highly explosive in the presence of air or water.

6. The size of the atom increases as you go down a column. What is the largest atom in column 16?

   polonium

7. The size of the atom decreases as you go across a row. What is the largest atom in row 3?

   sodium

Done

Name _____
Date _____

Lesson 2—What Are Metals?

A. Graphic Organizer

In the chart below, write the definition for each vocabulary word. Then give an example from the lesson that describes each word.

Vocabulary Word	Definition	Give an Example
metal	A substance that transfers heat and electricity well and is malleable.	iron
nonmetal	A substance that does not transfer heat and electricity well and is not malleable.	carbon
alloy	A solid solution in which a metal or nonmetal dissolves in a metal.	steel
metalloid	A substance that has some of the properties of a metal and some of the properties of a nonmetal.	silicon
malleable	Easy to shape or form.	aluminum

B. Write sentences

On the lines below, write a sentence for each of the words from the box.

malleable	metalloid	alloy

Sentences should reflect accurate use of the vocabulary words.

_____

_____

Name _____

Date _____ 12/12/17 ✓

Lesson 2—What Are Metals?

1. Investigation Skill Practice–Infer

Caleb's dad is a jeweler. He makes necklaces and earrings out of silver. To do this, he pounds the silver into the shapes he wants. What can you infer about the physical properties of silver that make it good to use for making jewelry?

Silver is malleable. It is shiny and attractive.

At Thanksgiving time, Anna's mother took out her good turkey platter. Anna noticed that it had brown stains on it. Her mother gave her a cloth and a special lotion to use to rub off the stains. What can you infer about the platter to explain why it got stains?

The platter was made of silver not of stainless steel. It does not have

the physical properties as stainless steel and it tarnishes.

2. Reading Skill Practice–Main Idea and Details

Read the selection. Underline the main idea. Write two details on the lines below.

If you lift the aluminum foil off the top of a steaming hot casserole, you will not burn your finger. The heat leaves the foil as soon as it no longer touches the hot substance. If you cover a bowl with aluminum foil, you can wrap it very tightly and press the edges of the foil to form a tight seal around the top. These two physical properties make aluminum foil very useful in the kitchen.

Details: Aluminum foil looses its heat as soon as it is out of contact with a hot substance. It can also mold to the top of a bowl to make a tight seal.

© Harcourt

Use with Unit 1.   (page 1 of 2)   Science Content Support   CS 35

Name _____

Date _____ Done

Lesson 2—What Are Metals?

Take Notes

Taking notes can help you remember important ideas.

- Write down important facts and ideas. Use your own words. You do not have to write in complete sentences.
- One way to organize notes is in a chart. Write down the main ideas in one column and facts and details in another.

As you read this lesson, use the chart below to take notes.

What Are Metals?	
Main Ideas	Fact
• metals have high thermal conductivity—they conduct heat well Students' main ideas should reflect content of lesson.	• a substance with high thermal conductivity could be used for a cooking pot

© Harcourt

Use with Unit 1.   Science Content Support   CS 34

Name _____

Date 01-10-18

Lesson 3—What Are the Properties of Some Common Substances?

A. Classify

Write the word *gas*, *liquid*, or *solid* on the line next to each situation.

1. You skate on the ice in the winter. — **solid**
2. A woman who faints is given oxygen. — **gas**
3. You use a graphite pencil to spell your name. — **solid**
4. You drink milk with your lunch. — **liquid**
5. A creek flows into the pond. — **liquid**
6. Steam rises from the teapot. — **gas**

B. Categorize

In each group below, one word does not belong in the same category as the others. Circle the letter of that word. Then identify the remaining items as types of solids, liquids, or gases.

1. a. oxygen
   b. neon
   c. hydrogen
   d. carbon (circled)
   types of gases

2. a. ice
   b. wood
   c. water (circled)
   d. sand
   types of solids

3. a. water
   b. iron (circled)
   c. mercury
   d. blood
   types of liquids

Name _____

Science Concepts

3. For each metal in the top column, put an X in the row that describes one of its physical properties.

	germanium	silicon	bronze	steel	tin	iron	silver
conducts heat well			X	X	X	X	X
conducts electricity well			X	X	X	X	X
does not conduct heat well	X	X					
does not conduct electricity well	X	X					
is a metalloid	X	X					
is an alloy			X	X			
is an element					X	X	X
looks shiny	X	X	X	X	X	X	X

4. On the lines below, tell what a scanning tunneling microscope (STM) is and why it is useful.

Answers should include an accurate definition and description of usefulness of the STM. Possible answer: The STM is a microscope designed to look at atoms. It is useful because it can detect impurities or weaknesses in metals.

© Harcourt

Science Content Support

Name _____

Date _____

Lesson 3—What Are the Properties of Some Common Substances?

Organize Information

Graphic organizers can help you organize information and make sense of the facts you read.

- Tables, charts, and webs are graphic organizers that can show main ideas and important details.
- Graphic organizers help you categorize, or group, information.
- Putting related ideas into categories makes it easier to find facts.

As you read the lesson, continue to add new facts and details to the organizer.

States of Matter

Gases

Air is a mixture of gases. **Answers should accurately reflect lesson content.**

Liquids

Water is most common liquid on the planet. **Answers should accurately reflect lesson content.**

Solids

Carbon is a common element on Earth. **Answers should accurately reflect lesson content.**

Molecules of Life

Plant and animal life depend on carbon. **Answers should accurately reflect lesson content.**

© Harcourt

Name _____

Date _____

Lesson 3—What Are the Properties of Some Common Substances?

1. Investigation Skill Practice–Infer

Bart tried to make an ice rink in his back yard by putting water into a wooden box. He made the box strong with long screws and thick wood. He was surprised that his box was broken in pieces when the water inside it froze. Make inferences to explain why the box broke.

The water inside the box expanded when it froze and broke the box apart.

2. Reading Focus Skill Practice–Main Idea and Details

Read the selection. Underline the main idea. Write 3 details on the lines below.

Most of the objects and substances on Earth are made up of only a very few elements. Some elements, such as carbon, oxygen, and hydrogen are part of almost everything you touch. However some common elements are deadly to humans even in small amounts. For example, mercury was once used in thermometers, but it is very poisonous when inhaled or eaten. Lead is also a poison. It can cause children to become ill. Today it cannot be used in paints or other substances that people may be exposed to. Although oxygen is not a poison, ozone, made from three oxygen atoms is deadly to people who breathe in even a small amount.

Details: Mercury is very poisonous when inhaled or eaten. Lead can cause children to become ill. Ozone is deadly to people who breathe in even a small amount.

© Harcourt

Name _____

Date _____

Lesson 4—How Are Chemical and Physical Properties Used?

A. Cloze Exercise

Study the words and their definitions below. Then, using the underlined context clues, fill in the blanks with one of the words. Use all of the words once.

> chemical property: A property that involves the way a substance combines with other substances to form new substances.
>
> acid: A chemical compound that turns blue litmus paper red and has a pH of less than 7
>
> base: A chemical compound that turns red litmus paper blue and has a pH of more than 7

1 The pH of the substance is 8. This substance is a(n) _____base_____ .

2. An organism, such as pH of 4. My blueberry bushes grow well in a(n) _____acid_____ soil.

3. One of the chemical properties of the iron is its ability to combine with oxygen to make rust.

B. Explore Word Meanings

Answer the questions.

1 Which of these pH readings are bases: 4.3, 8.5, 5.5, 7, and 7.5?
These readings are bases: 8.5 and 7.5.

2. What would you call an ore: a chunk of pure gold or a chunk of rock with minerals that you cannot identify?
An ore is the chunk of rock with minerals that you cannot identify.

Use with Unit 1   Science Content Support   CS 41

Name _____

Date _____

Science Concepts

3. Recall concepts in the lesson by answering the questions about the states of matter.

Gases

What are the two most important gases that make up our air?

nitrogen, oxygen

Give an example of a noble gas.

neon, krypton, argon, or xenon

Liquids

What happens to most liquids as they get cold?
They contract.

What is the only metal that stays in a liquid state at room temperature?

mercury

Solids

Name several compounds that contain carbon.

sugar, coal, petroleum, natural gas

What do charcoal, graphite, and diamonds have in common?
They are made up of carbon.

Molecules of Life

What are the five elements that make up DNA?

carbon, oxygen, hydrogen, nitrogen, and phosphorus

CS 40 Science Content Support   (page 2 of 2)   Use with Unit 1.

Name _____

Date _____

Lesson 4—How Are Chemical and Physical Properties Used?

1. Investigation Skill Practice—Draw Conclusions

You hold a magnet over a mixture of metal shavings. Some of them are drawn to the magnet. Others stay on the table. What conclusions can you draw about the metal shavings mixture? What additional tests could you do to identify all the metals in the mixture?

You can conclude that one of the metals in the mixture is not magnetic.

You would need to know additional information, such as the melting

point or the solubility of the metals before you could identify all of

them accurately.

2. Reading Focus Skill Practice—Main Idea and Details

Read the selection. Underline the main idea. Write two details on the lines below.

The pH level of your garden soil is very important to know because some plants grow better at certain levels of pH. There are two ways to adjust the pH of your soil. First, if your soil is too acidic, you must add calcium carbonate, often called lime. The lime has a base pH and when you mix it with your soil, your soil will become less acidic. Second, if your soil is too basic, you should add organic matter. Organic matter could be compost, manure, leaves, sawdust, or peat moss.

Details: If your soil is too acidic, you must add calcium carbonate,

often called lime. If your soil is too basic, you should add organic

matter, such as compost, manure, leaves, sawdust, or peat moss.

© Harcourt

Name _____

Date _____

Lesson 4—How Are Chemical and Physical Properties Used?

Done ✓

Preview and Question

Identifying main ideas in a lesson and asking question about them can help you find important information.

- To preview a lesson, read the lesson title and the section titles. Look at the pictures, and read their captions. Try to get an idea of the main topic and think of questions you have about the topic.
- Read to find the answers to your questions. Then recite, or say, the answers aloud. Finally, review what you have read.

As you read this lesson, fill in the chart and practice reading, reciting, and reviewing.

How Are Chemical and Physical Properties Used?				
Preview	Questions	Read	Recite	Review
Methods and reasons for separating mixtures	How does chemistry help scientists separate mixtures?	✓	✓	✓
Preview material should reflect content of the lesson.	Questions should be relevant to the content of the lesson.			

© Harcourt

Name

Date

Lesson 4—How Are Chemical and Physical Properties Used?

Acids, Bases, and Salts

A. The pH Scale

The pH scale shows how acidic or basic a solution is. It runs from 1, most acidic, to 14, most basic. Pure water is neither acidic nor basic and has a pH of 7.

strong acids   weak acids   neutral   weak bases   strong bases

1   2   3   4   5   6   7   8   9   10   11   12   13   14

strong hydrochloric acid   stomach acids   vinegar   soda   rainwater   milk   pure water   sea water   bleach   toothpaste   laundry detergent   ammonia   oven cleaner   strong sodium hydroxide

© Harcourt

Name

Science Concepts

3. For each test below, explain how the test is conducted and what the test shows.

Solubility

What does the test show?

It shows whether the substance dissolves in water.

How do you conduct the test?

You mix the substance with water.

Litmus paper

What does the test show?

It shows the pH of a substance.

How do you conduct the test?

The litmus paper turns from red to blue or blue to red when it touches a substance.

Flame test

What does the test show?

It shows what color the substance burns.

How do you conduct the test?

You dip a coil of wire into the substance and then hold it over a flame.

Melting point

What does the test show?

It shows when a substance turns from a solid to a liquid.

How do you conduct the test?

You heat the substance until it melts and measure the temperature at which melting occurs.

© Harcourt

Name _____

Use the pH scale to help answer these questions.

1. Is bleach an acid or base? __base__

2. Is soda an acid or base? __acid__

3. Of rainwater, vinegar, and milk, which is the most acidic? __vinegar__

4. Of seawater, ammonia, and bleach, which is the most basic (alkaline)? __ammonia__

5. Label the pH scale to identify where the strong acids are.
   [See labels above the pH scale.]

6. Label the pH scale to identify where the weak acids are.
   [See labels above the pH scale.]

7. Label the pH scale to identify where the strong bases are.
   [See labels above the pH scale.]

8. Label the pH scale to identify where the weak bases are.
   [See labels above the pH scale.]

9. Label the pH scale to identify where neutral is.
   [See labels above the pH scale.]

Name _____

B. Salts

The "salt" you add to food is just one example of a group of substances called salts. Salts form when a strong acid reacts with a strong base. Water can also form.

In this example, nitric acid and potassium hydroxide react to form potassium nitrate salt and water.

$$HNO_3 + KOH \rightarrow KNO_3 + H_2O$$

Look at how the elements on the left side of the reaction recombine to form the substances on the right.

$$HNO_3 + KOH \longrightarrow KNO_3 + HOH$$

The next example looks more complicated, but it still shows a strong acid and strong base making a salt and water. Sulfuric acid and potassium hydroxide react to form potassium sulfate salt and water. The same elements on the left end up on the right, but in different combinations.

$$H_2SO_4 + KOH \rightarrow K_2SO_4 + H_2O$$

1. What do you need to make a salt? __strong acid and a strong base__

2. What happens when a strong acid and a strong base react? __the elements of the acid and base recombine to form a salt and water__

3. If you combine stomach acid and oven cleaner, would the outcome be a salt and water? Explain. __Accept all reasonable answers. Students may argue that since stomach acid is a strong acid and oven cleaner is a strong base, they would react to form salt and water.__

Name _____

Date _____

Lesson 5—What Are Chemical Reactions?

A. Word Families

Fill in the blanks with the correct form of the word.

1. reactant/react

   Noun: One __reactant__ in the experiment was sodium. It combined with chlorine to make table salt.

   Verb: The elements iron and oxygen __react__ with each other in the presence of water to form rust.

2. salt/salty

   Noun: When a base and an acid come in contact, the result is some type of __salt__ .

   Adjective: The ocean water left a __salty__ taste after it dried from my skin.

3. product/produce

   Noun: What __product__ do you get from the combination of sodium and chlorine?

   Verb: The chemicals ammonia and bleach combine to __produce__ a terrible, poisonous gas.

4. chemical reaction/chemically reacting

   Adjective and noun: Sunlight, water, and air create a __chemical reaction__ in a plant to make its food.

   Adverb and verb: You can tell that the substances are __chemically reacting__ because they create bubbles and turn a different color.

B. Write Sentences

Write your own sentences using at least two words from the box.

chemical reaction	reactant	product	salt

Sentences should show the correct use of the vocabulary words.

_____

_____

Name _____

4. If you combine water and bleach, would the outcome be a salt and water? Explain. __Since the reactants are not a strong acid and strong base, the product will not be salt and water.__

5. Look at the pH scale. Identify two products that will likely combine to form a salt and water. __Students should identify a strong acid and strong base.__

6. Predict the formula for the salt that forms when the strong acid hydrochloric acid (HCl) and the strong base potassium hydroxide (KOH) react. Try to write the equation that represents the reaction.
   __KCl (potassium chloride); HCl + KOH → KCl + H$_2$O.__

Name _____

Date _____

Lesson 5—What Are Chemical Reactions?

Skim and Scan

Skimming and scanning are two ways to learn from what you read.

- To skim, quickly read the lesson title and the section titles. Look at the visuals, or images, and read the captions. Use this information to identify the main topics.
- To scan, look quickly through the text for specific details, such as key words or facts.

Before you read this lesson, skim the text to find the main ideas. Then look for key words. If you have questions about a topic, scan the text to find the answers. Fill in the chart below as you skim and scan.

What Are Chemical Reactions?	
Skim	Scan
Lesson Title: **What Are Chemical Reactions?**	Key Words and Facts: • **chemical reaction** • **reactant** • **product** • **salt** • **Facts should be accurately excerpted from the text.**
Main Idea: **During chemical reactions the atoms in the reactants rearrange to form products with different properties.**	
Section Titles: **Changing Properties, Reactants and Products, Making New Substances, Conservation of Mass, Salts**	
Visuals: **Golden Gate Bridge, Chemical Properties of Matter Chart, bread baking, table salt reaction, rust reaction, nitrogen dioxide reaction, tarnish, glow stick, common acids and bases, salt in the Earth's crust, ice cream maker using salt,**	

© Harcourt

Name _____

Date _____

Lesson 5—What Are Chemical Reactions?

1. Investigation Skill Practice—Develop a Testable Question

Juan noticed that when he made pancakes with baking powder, they were fluffy and fat. When he forgot to add baking powder to the pancake batter, his pancakes were flat and dense. What testable question could Juan develop about this observation? What procedure could he use to test his question?

Testable Question: **How does baking powder affect the finished**

pancakes?

Procedure: **He could make two pancakes, one with baking powder in**

the batter and the other without. Then he could compare and record

the results.

2. (Focus Skill) Reading Skill Practice—Compare and Contrast

Read the selection. Compare and contrast the ice on the steps and on the sidewalk.

Roadway ice is dangerous for motorists. Not all towns use the same methods for melting it. In some places, towns put salt on the roads. The salt makes the freezing temperature of water change. That way the roads stay wet instead of icy. However, salt can harm plants when it runs off the road. In other places, towns put down sand instead of salt. Sand is usually dark brown or black. The sand works with the sun to absorb heat and melt the ice. It also helps tires grip the slippery ice. The sand does not harm plants that grow near the streets.

Similarities: **Both methods solve the problem of slippery streets due**

to icy conditions.

Differences: **Salt lowers the freezing point of water. Sand absorbs**

heat from the sun and melts ice. Salt is harmful to plants; sand is

© Harcourt

Name _____

Date _____

Lesson 5—What Are Chemical Reactions?

Chemical Reactions

Physical properties can be observed without changing the type of substance. They include density and melting point. Chemical properties describe how a substance reacts with other substances, such as how it burns.

Physical changes do not produce new substances. They can be easily undone. Examples include folding paper or melting ice cubes. Chemical changes do produce new substances. They are difficult to undo. Examples include burning paper or adding acid to metal.

A. Consider each property in this chart. Check one column to show if it is a physical or chemical property.

Property	Physical?	Chemical?
1. texture	✓	
2. ability to rust		✓
3. volume	✓	
4. how it reacts to acid		✓
5. boiling point	✓	
6. color	✓	

B. Consider each change in this chart. Check one column to indicate if it is a physical or chemical change.

Change	Physical?	Chemical?
1. carving wood into a baseball bat	✓	
2. dissolving sugar in water	✓	
3. burning a candle		✓
4. freezing water into ice cubes	✓	
5. metal nail rusting		✓
6. tearing paper	✓	

Use with Unit 1.   (page 1 of 2)   Science Content Support

Name _____

Science Concepts

3. Identify each of the following as a physical change or a chemical change. Write *physical change* or *chemical change* on the line.

water turns to ice   **physical change**

a tomato rots in the refrigerator   **chemical change**

sugar dissolves in water   **physical change**

an iron gate becomes rusty   **chemical change**

4. Identify the reactants and the products in the following reactions.

Sodium + Chlorine = sodium chloride (table salt)

What are the reactants?   **sodium and chlorine**

What is the product?   **sodium chloride (table salt)**

iron + oxygen = rust (iron oxide)

What are the reactants?   **iron and oxygen**

What is the product?   **rust (iron oxide)**

5. When nitrogen dioxide is heated it splits into two elements.

What elements does it become?   **nitrogen and oxygen**

How does the mass of the nitrogen dioxide compare to the mass of the products of the chemical reaction?

The masses are the same.

6. When you combine the elements hydrogen and oxygen you get H_2O.

What compound have you created?   **water**

How does the mass of the hydrogen and the oxygen compare to the mass of the H_2O that is the product of the chemical reaction?

The masses are the same.

7. Answer the questions about salt.

What are the physical properties of salts?

Salts are hard and brittle.

How are salts formed?

They form a reaction between an acid and a base.

Science Content Support   (page 2 of 2)   Use with Unit 1.

Name _____

Date _____

Lesson 1—How Do Organisms Transport Materials?

A. Words with Multiple Meanings

Think about how the meaning of the underlined word is used in each sentence. Circle the correct definition.

1. Marie used a microscope to compare a plant <u>cell</u> and an animal <u>cell</u>.

   small, isolated room

   (basic unit of life)

2. Nervous <u>tissue</u> carries signals from the brain to parts of the body.

   (cells that carry out a certain function)

   sheet of absorbent paper

3. The heart is a hard-working <u>organ</u> that pumps blood to all parts of the body.

   musical instrument with sets of pipes controlled by a keyboard

   (group of tissues working together.)

B. Content Area Words

Write the letter of the definition that matches the word.

1. __f__ capillaries

2. __a__ organ system

3. __c__ nucleus

4. __d__ cytoplasm

5. __b__ organelles

6. __e__ vacuoles

a. a group of organs that work together to do a job for the body

b. structures within a cell with a specific function for keeping the cell alive

c. the organelle that directs all of a cell's activities

d. the jelly between the cell membrane and the nucleus

e. organelles that store nutrients, water, or waste materials until the cell uses them or gets rid of them

f. tiny blood vessels

© Harcourt

Use with Unit 2.

Science Content Support **CS 55**

Name _____

C. Iodine-Starch Reactions

The pictures below show the steps and results of an activity about iodine and starch. You will use it to answer the questions. You can also perform the investigation, if you have the proper materials and supervision.

ACTIVITY: Potatoes and Iodine

You will need:

- potato
- knife
- iodine solution
- eyedropper

If you place a few drops of iodine solution on the cut face of a potato, the solution will turn dark purple-black.

Identify each change in the investigation as physical or chemical:

1. cutting the potato __physical__

2. iodine solution changing color __chemical__

3. Potatoes are starchy foods. What does the color change in iodine indicate? __the presence of starch__

CS 54 Science Content Support (page 2 of 2) Use with Unit 1.

© Harcourt

Name _____

Date _____

Lesson 1—How Do Organisms Transport Materials?

Anticipation Guide

An anticipation guide can help you anticipate, or predict, what you will learn as you read.

- Look at the section titles for clues.
- Preview the Reading Check question at the end of each section. Use what you know about the subject of each section to predict the answers.
- Read to find out whether your predictions were correct.

As you read each section, complete the anticipation guide below. Predict answers to each question and check to see if your predictions were correct.

How Do Organisms Transport Materials?		
Cells as Building Blocks		
Reading Check	Prediction	Correct?
How do cells keep organisms alive and healthy?	In this section, we will learn about the function of cells.	✓
Cell Structures and Functions		
Reading Check	Prediction	Correct?
What organelle directs all the functions of a cell?	In this section we will learn the parts of a cell.	✓
Cells, Systems, Organs, Systems		
Reading Check	Prediction	Correct?
What life functions do tissues and organs carry out?	In this section we will learn how tissues and organs function in the body.	✓
Transport in Multicellular Organisms		
Reading Check	Prediction	Correct?
What are the functions of transport tissues in plants and animals?	In this section, we will learn how plants and animals move food and water from one area to another.	✓

Name _____

Date _____

Lesson 1—How Do Organisms Transport Materials?

1. Investigation Skill Practice–Classify

Look at the list of tissues in the box. Classify them in the chart under the correct type of tissue.

blood	cartilage	skin	the lining of
bones	muscles	spinal cord	your capillaries
brain	nerves	tongue muscle	

muscle tissue	epithelial tissue	connective tissue	nervous tissue
tongue muscle muscles	skin the lining of your capillaries	bones cartilage blood	brain nerves spinal cord

2. Reading Focus Skill Practice–Main Idea and Details

Read the selection. Underline the main idea. Write 3 details on the lines below.

Each system of the body is dependent on the others, but the circulatory system is the one that gets around the most. For example, the circulatory system gathers waste from each cell and delivers it to the excretory system. That's how wastes are eliminated from the body. It works with the respiratory system by collecting and distributing oxygen to every part of the body. It works with the digestive system by gathering nutrients from food and supplying them to all the organs and tissues.

Details: It gathers waste and delivers it to excretory system. It collects and distributes oxygen. It also gathers and supplies nutrients from food to the organs and tissues.

Page CS 59 (Vocabulary Power)

Name _____

Date _____

Lesson 2—How Do the Circulatory and Respiratory Systems Work Together?

A. Word Origins

Fill in the blank with the word from the box that fits the word origin. Use a dictionary if you need help.

circulatory system	arteries	veins
respiratory system	capillaries	

Word Origin	Language	Meaning	Vocabulary Word
1. *arteria*	Greek	to lift, take up	artery
2. *capillus*	Latin	hair	capillaries
3. *vena*	Latin	vein	vein
4. *circulatus*	Latin	to make a circle	circulatory system
5. *respirare*	Latin	of breathing	respiratory system

B. Context Clues

Use context clues to complete each sentence correctly.

1. The blood vessels that carry blood away from the heart are ___arteries___ .

2. Breathing smog, pollution, or smoke can cause problems in your ___respiratory system___ .

3. Blocked or hardened blood vessels put a burden on a person's ___circulatory system___ .

4. The heart pumps the blood that returns from the body's organs through large ___veins___ .

Use with Unit 2.   Science Content Support

© Harcourt

Page CS 58 (Science Concepts)

Name _____

Science Concepts

3. Read the list of details explaining how an organism transports materials. Write each detail that applies to plants under *Plant Cells*. Write each detail that applies to animals under *Animal Cells*. Some may apply to both.

Details

Cells contain a nucleus, cell membrane, and cytoplasm.

The transport system includes the heart, blood vessels, and blood.

The transport system carries water and minerals from roots to leaves.

The transport system helps carryout the removal of wastes.

The transport system helps deliver oxygen throughout the organism.

Organisms have specialized tissues that serve different functions.

Cells work together to carry out life functions.

Animal Cells	Plant Cells
Cells contain a nucleus, cell membrane, and cytoplasm.	Cells contain a nucleus, cell membrane, and cytoplasm.
The transport system includes the heart, blood vessels, and blood.	The transport system carries water and minerals from roots to leaves.
The transport system helps carry out the removal of wastes.	The transport system helps carryout the removal of wastes.
The transport system helps deliver oxygen throughout the organism.	The transport system helps deliver oxygen throughout the organism.
Organisms have specialized tissues that serve different functions.	Organisms have specialized tissues that serve different functions.
Cells work together to carry out life functions.	Cells work together to carry out life functions.

4. Name two more functions of plant and animal cells that were not on the list of details above.

Sentences should contain accurate information from the lesson.

Science Content Support   (page 2 of 2)   Use with Unit 2.

© Harcourt

Name _____

Date _____

Lesson 2—How Do the Circulatory and Respiratory Systems Work Together?

Pose Questions

Posing, or asking, questions as you read can help you understand what you are reading.

- Form questions as you read. For example, you may ask how a science concept is connected to other concepts.
- Use the questions to guide you reading. Look for answers as you read.

Before you read this lesson, write a list of questions in the chart below. Look for the answers as you read. Record the answers in the chart.

How Do the Circulatory and Respiratory Systems Work Together?	
Questions	Answers
How does the air I breathe get into my blood?	Tiny air sacs in the lungs pass the oxygen to the blood through the capillaries, or tiny blood vessels.
Questions should be relevant to lesson content.	Answers should accurately answer question.

Name _____

Date _____

Lesson 2—How Do the Circulatory and Respiratory Systems Work Together?

1. **Investigation Skill Practice–Identify the Dependent and Controlled Variables**

   Janet wants to determine how different people respond to exercise. She chooses one athlete from the track team, one athlete from the golf team, and one person who does not regularly exercise. She tracks their heart rate three times: once sitting, once after walking for five minutes, and once after running for five minutes.

   What is the controlled variable in Janet's experiment?

   the activity

   What is the dependent variable in Janet's experiment?

   the level of regular exercise among the people being tested

2. **Reading Focus Skill Practice–Sequence**

   Put the following events about the respiratory system in the correct sequence. Number the steps 1 to 4.

   2 Clean air travels down your trachea, into smaller and smaller tubes into your lungs.

   4 Carbon dioxide leaves your body when you exhale.

   3 Carbon dioxide passes from the blood plasma into the air sacs in the lungs while oxygen passes from the air sacks into the blood.

   1 You breathe air in through your nose.

Name _____
Date _____

Lesson 3—How Do the Organs of the Digestive System Work Together?

A. Word Origins

Learning the origins of a word sometimes helps you remember its meaning. Fill in the table with the correct vocabulary word from the box.

digest	esophagus	peristalsis	villi	intestine

Word Origin	Language	Meaning	Vocabulary Word
oisophagos	Latin	passage for food	1. esophagus
peristaltikos	Greek	to surround	2. peristalsis
vellus	Latin	shaggy hair	3. villi
digestus	Latin	to arrange	4. digest
intestinus	Latin	inward, internal	5. intestine

B. Context Clues

Complete the sentence with the correct word or phrase from the box.

digestive system	esophagus	peristalsis

1. If you are an athlete, you know how important it is to keep your __digestive system__ healthy by eating lots of fruits and vegetables.

2. Toys with small parts are a choking hazard because they can get stuck in a child's __esophagus__.

3. The movement called __peristalsis__ helps move food from the stomach through the intestines to the colon.

Use with Unit 2.   Science Content Support   CS 63

© Harcourt

Name _____

Science Concepts

3. Read the events that occur in the relationship between the circulatory and the respiratory systems below. Write them in the correct order in the flow chart.

The heart pumps the returned blood to the lungs.

Oxygen moves into capillaries from the lungs.

Air is breathed in through the nose or mouth.

Capillaries allow oxygen to move into cells and waste materials to move out.

Oxygen-rich blood goes to the heart.

The heart pumps blood out through the arteries.

Blood flows from the arteries into capillaries.

Blood is returned to the heart through veins.

Air travels through the trachea into the lungs.

Oxygen moves into capillaries from the lungs.

Oxygen-rich blood goes to the heart.

The heart pumps blood out through the arteries.

Blood flows from the arteries into capillaries.

Capillaries allow oxygen to move into cells and waste materials to move out.

Blood is returned to the heart through veins.

The heart pumps the returned blood to the lungs.

Air is breathed in through the nose or mouth.

Air travels through the trachea into the lungs.

CS 62   Science Content Support   (page 2 of 2)   Use with Unit 2.

© Harcourt

Name _____
Date _____

Lesson 3—How Do the Organs of the Digestive System Work Together?

Use Visuals

Visuals can help you better understand and remember what you read.

- Photographs, illustrations, diagrams, charts, and maps are different kinds of visuals.
- Many visuals have titles, captions, or labels that help readers understand what is shown.
- Visuals often show information that appears in the text, but they show it in a different way.

As you read this lesson, look closely at the visuals and the text that goes with them. Answer the questions in the checklist.

How Do the Organs of the Digestive System Work Together?
What kind of visual is shown to illustrate the digestive system? **A drawing of the digestive tract inside a human with labels of each organ.**
What does the visual show? **It shows the organs involved in the process of digesting food inside a human body.**
How does the visual relate to the lesson you are reading? **The visual shows the name and position of each organ in the digestive system.**
How does the visual help you better understand the subject of what you are reading? **Answers should show reflection about why the visual is helpful.**

Name _____
Date _____

Lesson 3—How Do the Organs of the Digestive System Work Together?

1. Investigation Skill Practice—Observe, Record Data, and Make Inferences

Jill covered the inside of a strainer with a thin cloth. Then she placed a scoop of plain yogurt over the cloth. She watched and took note of what happened every ten minutes for one hour. She noticed that the liquid from the yogurt dripped out through the cloth into a bowl below.

What did Jill observe?
She observed the moisture dripping from the yogurt through the cloth.

When did Jill record her data?
She watched the yogurt every ten minutes for one hour.

What inferences do you think Jill could make about how nutrients move from the intestines into the blood?
She can infer that over time, some parts of the food in the intestines will seep through the thin walls of the capillaries of the villi into the blood.

2. Reading Skill Practice—Sequence

Put the following events about the process of digestion in the correct sequence. Number the steps 1 to 5.

4 Food is churned and mixed with chemicals that break it down.

3 Food travels to the stomach through the esophagus.

1 Chewing breaks food down.

5 Broken down food travels out of the stomach to the intestine.

2 Saliva in the mouth begins digestion of starches.

Name _____
Date _____

Lesson 4—How Do Plants and Animals Rid Themselves of Wastes?

A. Graphic Organizer

Fill in the blanks of the graphic organizer with details from the definition of each vocabulary word.

Vocabulary Word	Plants or Animals?	Function in Eliminating Wastes
urea	animals	waste carried by the blood
nephrons	animals	filters that remove urea, water, and other wastes from blood
stomata	plants	the holes under leaves that allow wastes to leave plants
ureters	animals	the tube that urine flows through
transpiration	plants	process that eliminates waste from plants
kidney	animals	main organ of excretory system, filters blood

B. Context Clues

Write the word or phrase from the box that best completes each sentence.

transpiration	kidneys	excretory system

1. When the woman's __kidneys__ failed, she began treatment to have her blood filtered by a machine.

2. The plant's ability to perform __transpiration__ means that it can eliminate water through holes in its leaves.

3. Your body stays healthy because its wastes are removed by your __excretory system__.

Use with Unit 2.

© Harcourt

Name _____

Science Concepts

3. Events in a Sequence

Tell what happens in each organ of the digestive system listed below.

mouth
Food mixes with saliva and is ground up by the teeth.

esophagus
Food travels from the mouth to the stomach through the esophagus.

stomach
Food is mixed with digestive juices.

small intestine
Chemicals mix with digested food from the stomach and nutrients are taken out.

large intestine
Peristalsis moves food from small intestine to large intestine. Water is reabsorbed into the body. Remaining food moves to the colon.

colon
The body's wastes are eliminated from the body.

4. How does the digestive process start in your mouth?
The saliva in our mouths starts to break down the starches in the food we eat.

© Harcourt

Name _____
Date _____

Unit 2, Lesson 4

Lesson 4—How Do Plants and Animals Rid Themselves of Wastes?

Make an Outline

An outline is a good way to record main ideas and details.

• Topics in an outline are shown by Roman numerals.
• Main ideas about each topic are shown by capital letters.
• Details about each main idea are identified by numbers.

As you read this lesson, remember to pay attention to the topics, main ideas, and details. Use the information to complete the outline below.

How Do Plants and Animals Rid Themselves of Wastes?

I. The Excretory System
  A. Wastes are removed by the excretory system.
    1. Carbon dioxide is removed when you exhale. _____
    2. Ammonia is removed in the urine. _____
  B. The excretory system is made up of kidneys, ureters, bladder, and urethra.
    1. The kidneys are the main organ. _____
    2. Nephrons filter urea, water, and other wastes from the body. _____
    3. Urine flows through ureters to the bladder. _____
    4. Urine flows out of the bladder through the urethra. _____
II. How Plants Rid Themselves of Waste
  A. Plants must also eliminate wastes like animals do.
    1. Some plants store wastes in organs that fall off, such as leaves. _____
    2. Others store wastes in a vacuole of each cell. _____
  B. Waste materials in plants are oxygen and water.
    1. The wastes leave through stomata. _____
    2. Water leaves through transpiration. _____

CS 68   Science Content Support   Use with Unit 2.

Name _____
Date _____

Unit 2, Lesson 4

Lesson 4—How Do Plants and Animals Rid Themselves of Wastes?

1. Investigation Skill Practice—Record Data, Make Inferences

Louis wondered how different plants eliminate waste. He studied the life cycles of many plants, such as tulips, pine trees, maple trees, palm trees, and house plants. He noticed that some plants drop leaves during cool weather. Others die back after blooming. Some do not drop leaves at all and never appear to die.

What data should Louis record as he makes his observations?

He should note which plants lose leaves, die back, or do not lose

leaves during their life cycle.

What inferences can Louis make about how different plants rid themselves of waste?

He can infer that all plants have wastes, but each plant eliminates

waste in a different way.

2. Reading Focus Skill Practice—Compare and Contrast

Read the selection. Compare and contrast a dialysis machine and the kidneys.

When a person's kidneys do not function properly, he or she may go on dialysis. The dialysis machine works like a kidney. It forces all of the body's blood through a filter. It also separates waste material as a kidney would do. Although its function is similar, the experience is much different. While kidneys work all day and night, a dialysis machine filters the blood only three times each week. With kidneys, blood stays inside the body to be filtered. On a dialysis machine, blood must be taken out of the body, filtered, and then put back in. The procedure is uncomfortable, but for many, it is their only hope for life.

Similarities: Both kidneys and a dialysis machine filter blood and

separate waste material from the blood. Differences: The kidneys

work all day and night. Dialysis machines work three times each

week. Kidneys filter the blood inside the body. Dialysis machines

force the blood out of the body and then replace it after it is filtered.

Use with Unit 2.   (page 1 of 2)   Science Content Support   **CS 69**

Page CS 71 (Vocabulary Power)

Name _____

Date _____

Vocabulary Power

Unit 2, Lesson 5

Lesson 5—How Are Materials Transported in Vascular Plants?

A. Word Origins/Etymology

Write the word from the box that fits the word origin.

xylem	phloem	vascular tissue

1. A word that derives from *xylon*, the Greek word for "wood."
   xylem

2. A word that derives from *phloos*, the Greek word for "bark."
   phloem

3. A word that comes from *vasculum*, the Latin word for "small vessel."
   vascular tissue

B. Explore Word Meanings

For each description below, write *vascular plant* or *nonvascular plant*.

1. A plant without roots — nonvascular plant

2. A plant with a taproot — vascular plant

3. A plant without leaves or stems — nonvascular plant

4. A plant that can carry nutrients to each part — vascular plant

5. A plant that grows a ring of xylem each year — vascular plant

© Harcourt

Use with Unit 2.   Science Content Support   **CS 71**

Page CS 70 (Science Concepts)

Name _____

Science Concepts

3. Answer the questions in the chart for animals and plants. Be as specific as possible. Use your book if you need help.

	Animals	Plants
What wastes are produced?	carbon dioxide, ammonia	oxygen and water
Where are wastes stored?	in the bladder and colon	in a large central vacuole that stores waste until it is removed
How are wastes eliminated?	Lungs exhale waste gases. Kidneys filter waste from blood and water. Kidney sends waste water to the bladder where it is eliminated.	Waste air and water move out of plant through stomata in leaves. Water leaves through transpiration.
What are the parts of the excretory system?	kidneys, ureters, bladder, and urethra	

4. Answer the questions about how animals and plants eliminate wastes.

What is the function of the kidneys in animals?
The kidneys filter urea, water, and other wastes from the blood.

How do the stomata help a plant eliminate waste?
The stomata are tiny holes on the under side of leaves that allow water and oxygen to be released to the air.

© Harcourt

CS 70 Science Content Support   (page 2 of 2)   Use with Unit 2.

CS 70–CS 71   Science Content Support

PG. 191

Name _____

Date _____

Lesson 5—How Are Materials Transported in Vascular Plants?

1. Investigation Skill Practice—Infer

In early spring, when the sap begins to flow, a farmer puts her taps in the trunks of her sugar maple trees. These taps allow a thin sweet sap to drip slowly into a bucket. The farmer empties the buckets every day. After several weeks, she has collected a great cauldron of sap. She boils down the sap to make real maple syrup. What can you infer about the maple syrup process?

What part of the tree do the taps go into?

the xylem just under the bark

_____

Why is the sap sweet?

The leaves have made the sugar and it is being transported by the

phloem. Some of it leaks out through the tap.

2. Reading Focus Skill Practice—Main Idea and Details

Read the selection. Underline the main idea. Write 3 details on the lines below.

Like any plant, a grape vine has specific needs that must be met to make it thrive. First, grape vines require very deep soil because they have long roots that reach far below the surface of the earth. Second, grape vines grow best in places with a long, warm growing season. This allows the plant to set fruit and ripen before it gets too cold. Finally, grapes need good air circulation, such as a windy spot on a hill. Without good circulation, leaves cannot release their moisture, and the plant and fruit may rot before it gets ripe.

Details: Grape vines need deep soil, a long, warm growing season,

and good air circulation to be healthy.

_____

Use with Unit 2.   (page 1 of 2)   Science Content Support   **CS 73**

© Harcourt

Name _____

Date _____

Lesson 5—How Are Materials Transported in Vascular Plants?

Connect Ideas

You can use a web organizer to show how different ideas and information are related.

- List important themes in the ovals in the web's center.
- Add ovals showing main ideas that support each theme.
- Add bubbles for the details that support each main idea.

Complete the web below as you read this lesson. Fill in each bubble by adding facts and details. Add more bubbles if you need them.

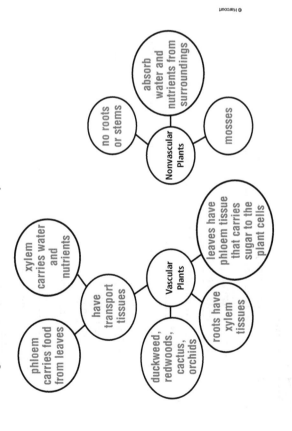

- no roots or stems
- absorb water and nutrients from surroundings
- Nonvascular Plants
- mosses

- xylem carries water and nutrients
- phloem carries food from leaves
- have transport tissues
- Vascular Plants
- duckweed, redwoods, cactus, orchids
- roots have xylem tissues
- leaves have phloem tissue that carries sugar to the plant cells

CS 72 Science Content Support   Use with Unit 2.

© Harcourt

Name _____

Date _____

Lesson 6—How Do Cells Get the Energy They Need?

Cloze Exercise

Study the words and their definitions below. Then, using context clues, fill in the blanks with one of the words. Use all of the words once.

> **photosynthesis:** the process by which plants make food from carbon dioxide and water and release oxygen into the air
>
> **cellular respiration:** the process by which cells use oxygen to break down sugar to release energy
>
> **fermentation:** the process that releases energy from sugar in the absence of oxygen
>
> **chlorophyll:** green pigment in a plant that allows a plant cell to use light to make food

In the fall, when the trees loose their green pigment, the leaf cells lose their __chlorophyll__ .

The process of __fermentation__ occurs during yogurt production in the absence of oxygen.

You might say that the energy you feel comes from the break down of sugar called __cellular respiration__ .

Animals depend on __photosynthesis__ because the process releases oxygen to the air for animals to breathe.

Use with Unit 2.   Science Content Support   CS 75

© Harcourt

Name _____

Science Concepts

3. Read the questions below. Write the word *leaves, stems,* or *roots* to answer the question. Some questions will have more than one answer.

What parts do vascular plants have that nonvascular plants do not?

__roots, stems and leaves__

What part uses sunlight, air and water to make sugar?

__leaves__

What part of the plant contains phloem that carries the sugar to the rest of the plant?

__leaves__

What part provides support for a plant?

__stems and roots__

Where does the vascular tissue gather in rings that show the age of a tree?

__stems__

What part absorbs water and nutrients from the soil?

__roots__

What parts of the plant contains vascular tissue?

__roots, stems and leaves__

What part has chloroplasts for making food?

__leaves__

What part anchors the plant to the ground?

__roots__

4. What is the function of xylem and phloem? Write your explanation on the lines below.

__Xylem is the vascular tissue that carries water and nutrients to__

__the rest of the plant. Phloem is the vascular tissue that transports__

__sugar from the leaves to all the other parts of the plant.__

CS 74   Science Content Support   (page 2 of 2)   Use with Unit 2.

© Harcourt

Name _____

Date _____

Lesson 6—How Do Cells Get the Energy They Need?

Take Notes

Taking notes can help you remember important ideas.

- Write down important facts and ideas. Use your own words. You do not have to write in complete sentences.
- One way to organize notes is in a chart. Write down the main ideas in one column and facts and details in another.

As you read this lesson, use the chart below to take notes.

How Do Cells Get the Energy They Need?	
Main Ideas	Facts
• Photosynthesis is the process that makes food for the plant.	• The process of photosynthesis supplies enough oxygen into the air for humans to breathe.
• Students' main ideas should reflect content of lesson.	• Students' facts should support main ideas.
•	•
•	•

Name _____

Date _____

Lesson 6—How Do Cells Get the Energy They Need?

1. Investigation Skill Practice–Identify the Independent Variable

Kaylee conducted an experiment with two identical plants. She planted both plants in rich soil. She put both plants in a sunny window. To one plant, she gave three tablespoons of water three times each day. To the other plant, she gave one tablespoon of water once each day. She observed how both plants grew.

What is Kaylee studying in her experiment?

She is studying the effect of water on the growth of a plant.

What is the independent variable in Kaylee's experiment?

The independent variable is the amount of water she gives to each

plant.

2. Reading Skill Practice–Sequence

Put the following events about the process of photosynthesis and cellular respiration in the correct sequence. Number the steps 1 to 5.

_4_ Plants use carbon dioxide and water to make sugar during photosynthesis.

_1_ An animal breathes oxygen from the air.

_3_ Water and carbon dioxide are released as waste.

_5_ Oxygen and water are released as waste.

_2_ Oxygen helps turn sugars to energy in the mitochondria.

Page 1

Name _____

Date _____

Lesson 6—How Do Cells Get the Energy They Need?

A. Photosynthesis and Respiration

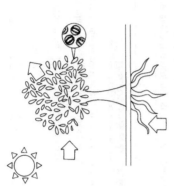

The picture above shows how a plant captures energy and stores it in the process of photosynthesis. Describe how each word below is a part of your description. You may use drawings and labels as a part of your description.

1. oxygen

   Answer should reflect that oxygen is a waste product that is released from the plant into the air during photosynthesis.

2. water

   Answer should reflect that water is taken in by the plant and used during photosynthesis.

3. sunlight

   Answer should reflect that the plant absorbs energy from sunlight and uses that energy to split the water molecules and form food.

4. carbon dioxide

   Answer should reflect that carbon dioxide is taken in from the air by the plant as part of photosynthesis. The carbon molecules combine with hydrogen from the water to make glucose or sugar food.

Use with Unit 2.   (page 1 of 2)   Science Content Support   **CS 79**

Page 2

Name _____

Science Concepts

3. **Identify the Sequence**

   The events of photosynthesis are similar to the events in cellular respiration. Read the events listed in the chart and copy each event under *Photosynthesis* or *Cellular Respiration*. Put the events in the correct order under each heading.

   > Carbon dioxide and water are released into the blood.
   >
   > Carbon dioxide combines with hydrogen from the water to make glucose.
   >
   > Carbon dioxide is exhaled through the lungs.
   >
   > Glucose is used for food.
   >
   > Oxygen in the mitochondria breaks down sugar.
   >
   > Oxygen and water is released into the air.
   >
   > Sunlight is absorbed by chloroplasts.
   >
   > The energy from the sun causes water molecules to split.
   >
   > Water is carried to the kidneys.
   >
   > When sugar breaks down, it releases energy.

Photosythesis
Sunlight is absorbed by chloroplasts.
The energy causes water molecules to split.
Carbon dioxide combines with hydrogen from the water to make glucose.
Glucose is used for food.
Oxygen and water are released into the air.

Cellular Respiration in Animal Cells
Oxygen in the mitochondria breaks down sugar.
When sugar breaks down, it releases energy.
Carbon dioxide and water are released into the blood.
Carbon dioxide is exhaled through the lungs.
Water is carried to the kidneys.

CS 78   Science Content Support   (page 2 of 2)   Use with Unit 2.

© Harcourt

Name _____

Date _____

Lesson 1—How Does Water Move from Earth to the Air and Back Again?

A. Explore Word Meanings

Match the word on the left to its definition on the right.

1. __f__ evaporation   **a.** a word for the water cycle

2. __a__ hydrologic cycle   **b.** huge sheets of ice

3. __g__ condensation   **c.** a cloud that forms near the ground

4. __c__ fog   **d.** the constant movement of water from Earth's surface to the atmosphere and back to Earth's surface

5. __d__ water cycle   **e.** the gas form of water

6. __b__ glaciers   **f.** the process by which a liquid changes into a gas

7. __e__ water vapor   **g.** the process by which a gas changes into a liquid

B. Context Clues

Complete the sentence with a word from the box.

water vapor	condensation	evaporation

1. The night temperature was freezing, so __water vapor__ in the air inside the car froze to the inside of the car windows.

2. We turned on the heat, and as the windows warmed up, the ice melted and gathered as wet drops of __condensation__ on the windows.

3. Soon the car was toasty warm inside which allowed __evaporation__ to take place. The windows were dry again.

© Harcourt

Use with Unit 3.   Science Content Support

Name _____

B. Respiration Equation

Use the equation and what you already know about cellular respiration to answer the questions below.

The chemical equation for cellular respiration is:

$$C_6H_{12}O_6 + 6O_2 \rightarrow 6CO_2 + 6H_2O + \text{energy}$$

1. Which organisms use cellular respiration?

   Plants and animals use cellular respiration.

2. What purpose does cellular respiration serve for the organisms that perform it?

   Cellular respiration releases energy.

3. Use the chemical equation above to write a series of steps that describes what is happening in the process of cellular respiration. Be sure to tell which materials are taken in and which materials are released as part of the process.

   $C_6H_{12}O_6$ is glucose that is stored in plants. The organism takes in O_2, which is oxygen from the air, and uses it to break apart the glucose molecules. As energy is released for the organism to use, carbon dioxide CO_2 is released as a waste product, along with water, H_2O.

4. What happens to the waste products of respiration in the human body?

   Carbon dioxide is carried to the lungs and released into the air. Water is carried to the kidneys where it is released in urine.

Science Content Support   (page 2 of 2)   Use with Unit 2.

Science Content Support   **CS 80–CS 81**

Name _____

Date _____

Lesson 1—How Does Water Move from Earth to the Air and Back Again?

Use a K-W-L Chart

A K-W-L chart can help you focus on what you already know about a topic and what you want to learn about it.

- Use the K column to list what you already know about the water cycle.
- Use the W column to list what you want to learn about the water cycle.
- Use the L column to list what you have learned about the water cycle from your reading.

Complete your own K-W-L chart as you read this lesson.

How Does Water Move from Earth to the Air and Back Again?		
What I Know	**What I Want to Learn**	**What I Learned**
• I know that ocean water is salty and cannot be used for drinking.	• How does it get salty? • Where does fresh water come from?	• Statements should contain accurate information from the lesson.
• Statements should reflect students' common knowledge. •	• Questions should show thoughtful reflection. • Some questions may not be answered in the lesson. •	• Statements should contain accurate information from the lesson. •

© Harcourt

Name _____

Date _____

Lesson 1—How Does Water Move from Earth to the Air and Back Again?

1. Investigation Skill Practice—Draw Conclusions

Miguel noticed something on his bus ride to school in the morning. He noticed that when the bus drove through a valley between two hills, it often drove through thick fog. He noticed that the fog was only around on cool mornings, and it was always gone by the afternoon when the sun was shining. What conclusions can you draw from Miguel's observations?

Possible answers: Fog collects in low places. Fog forms when the air has not become warm from the sun. Fog evaporates when the sun warms the air.

2. Reading Skill Practice—Main Idea and Details

Read the selection. Underline the main idea. List the details on the lines below.

Some scientists believe that they can use the sun to convert salt water to fresh water. They know that developing such a process would have advantages and disadvantages. First, the energy to make the fresh water would be cheap, since the sun's energy is free. Second, the source of ocean water is endless. There is more water in the ocean than is needed on land. However, the water conversion equipment would take a lot of money to build. Also, it could be costly to pump the fresh water to the cities or dry farmlands where it is needed.

Details: The energy to make the freshwater is free from the sun.

There is plenty of water in the ocean. But, the equipment would be expensive and it would be costly to pump it where it is needed.

© Harcourt

Name _____

Science Concepts

3. Answer the Questions

Why is Earth called the water planet?

Most of the Earth's surface is covered in water

Where is most of the water on Earth?

It is in the ocean.

How do we get fresh water?

Water is evaporated from the ocean, carried over land and dropped as

fresh water that collects in lakes, rivers, streams, and underground.

4. On the lines below, write the steps in the water cycle.

1. Water turns to vapor and is lifted into the air when it is warmed by

   the sun.

2. Vapor cools and becomes liquid.

3. When droplets become heavy enough, they fall as rain.

4. Some water is recycled back into the atmosphere and turns to water

   vapor again.

5. Write *evaporation* or *condensation* to describe what happens in each sentence below.

Your cold glass becomes wet when it stands outside on a hot day. **condensation**

Sweat dries from your face. **evaporation**

The birdbath you filled last week is now dry and empty. **evaporation**

Name _____

Date _____

Lesson 2—How Do Californians Get the Water they Need?

A. Compound Words

Write the word or phrase that fits the description below.

watershed	groundwater	water table

1. Compound word describing an area that sheds water off its surface **watershed**

2. Compound word identifying water that is underground **groundwater**

3. Phrase describing the underground table where water pools **water table**

B. Word Origins

Answer the questions about word origins.

1. The Greek word *hydor* means "water." How would you define *hydroelectric*?
   ***Hydroelectric* means making electricity from water**

2. The Latin word *aquae* means "water," and a duct is a type of tube or channel. How would you define *aqueduct*?
   ***Aqueduct* means a tube or channel that carries water.**

3. The Latin word *reservare* means "to hold back." How would you define *reservoir*?
   ***Reservoir* means an area of storage, in this case for water.**

C. Analogies

Fill in the blanks with one of the words from the box.

dam	aqueduct

dam _____ is to *hydroelectric power* as *solar panels* are to *solar power*

aqueduct _____ is to *water* as *pipeline* is to *natural gas*

Name _____

Date _____

Lesson 2—How Do Californians Get the Water they Need?

1. Investigation Skill Practice—Plan and Conduct an Investigation

Nancy was worried that she used too much water. She planned an experiment to find out how much water she could save by investigating with a simple water-saving plan. First, she measured how much water came from the tap while she brushed her teeth. Then she brushed her teeth using a cup of water instead. She measured how much water she saved. She calculated how much water she could save if she did the same thing every day. That's a lot of water!

What was Nancy's plan for her investigation?

Nancy planned to measure the amount of water conserved by using a

cup of water rather than turning the tap on to brush her teeth.

How did she conduct her investigation?

She measured the amount of water she used when the tap was on.

Then she measured how much water she used in a cup. She calculated

the amount she saved and how much she would save if she did the

same thing every day for the whole year.

2. Reading Skill Practice—Main Idea and Details

Read the selection. Underline the main idea. Write 3 details on the lines below.

Families who draw their water from a well take extra care to conserve water outside and inside their homes. They often plant native species of plants so that they do not need to water their lawn. They collect rain water to feed their animals and wash their cars. They also use water wisely by taking short showers, turning off water when it is not being used, and by washing only full loads of laundry.

Details: Families plant native species of plants, collect rain water to

feed their animals, take short showers, turn off water, and wash full

loads of laundry.

Use with Unit 3.   (page 1 of 2)   Science Content Support   **CS 87**

© Harcourt

Name _____

Date _____

Lesson 2—How Do Californians Get the Water they Need?

Understanding Vocabulary

Using a dictionary can help you learn new words that you find as you read.

- A dictionary shows all the meanings of a word and tells where the word came from.
- You can use a chart to list and organize unfamiliar words that you look up in a dictionary.

As you read this lesson, look up unfamiliar words in the dictionary. Add them to the chart below. Fill in each column to help you remember the word's meaning.

dam (DAM) *n.* [ME < MDu *dam*, ON *dammr*, <L *facere*] 1 a barrier built to hold back flowing water 2 the water thus kept back
[adapted from *Webster's Third College Edition*]

Word	Syllables	Origin	Definition
watershed	WAWT•er•shed	compound word. *Water* comes from German	The area of land in which water runs off into a particular system of creeks and rivers
Reservoir	REZ•er•vwahr	French	A body of water stored for future use
Aqueduct	AK•wuh•duhkt	Latin	A pipe or channel that is used to transport water
groundwater	GROWND•wawt•er	compound word. *Ground* is from German	Water that is in soil and rocks below Earth's surface

CS 86   Science Content Support   Use with Unit 3.

© Harcourt

Name _____

Date _____

Lesson 3—How Can People Conserve Water?

A. The Suffix –tion

The suffix –tion changes the meaning of the base word to which it is added. The suffix –tion means, "the act of [doing something]" or "the thing that is [being done]" or "the state of being [a certain way]."

Read each base word in the table. Choose the word from the box that is the base word plus the suffix –tion, and write it in the table. Then write its meaning. You can use a glossary to help you.

pollution	conservation	reclamation	irrigation

Base Word	New Word	Meaning
1. irrigate	irrigation	The act of watering land to grow crops
2. pollute	pollution	Any change to a resource that makes the resource unhealthful to use
3. conserve	conservation	The preserving and protecting of a resource
4. reclaim	reclamation	The recycling of used water

B. Explore Word Meanings

Circle the word that answers the question.

1. What phrase describes the safety of water for use by humans, animals, and plants?

water table   (water quality)   watershed

2. What is the word for a period of little rain?

summer   desert   (drought)

Use with Unit 3.   Science Content Support   CS 89

© Harcourt

Name _____

Science Concepts

3. Fill out the chart below by explaining if the type of water supply to the left is made by humans or nature and how it helps supply water.

	How Do Californians Get the Water they Need?	
	Made by Humans or Nature?	How does it help supply water to Californians?
lakes and rivers	nature	provides drinking water when season is rainy or snow is melting
watershed	nature	collects water from large area and routes it into lakes and rivers
aqueduct	humans	used to transport water from reservoir to humans
reservoirs	humans	holds water for humans to use during dry seasons
groundwater	nature	supplies drinking water from underground
aquifers	nature	allows wells to collect large amounts of water
wells	humans	draw water from aquifers

4. On the lines below, explain why saltwater is a valuable resource to Californians.

Saltwater provides food for people, sea salt, drinking water when salt
is removed, and it is used for recreation.

© Harcourt

CS 88   Science Content Support   (page 2 of 2)   Use with Unit 3.

Name _____

Date _____

Lesson 3—How Can People Conserve Water?

Write to Learn

Writing about what you read can help you better understand and remember information.

- Writing down the information that you learn from each lesson leads you to think about the information.
- Writing your own response to the new information makes it more meaningful to you.

As you read the lesson, pay attention to new and important information. Keep track of the information and your responses in the log below.

How Can People Conserve Water?	
What I Learned	**Personal Response**
Whatever I pour down the drain will end up in a body of water.	Now I understand how water can get polluted by people who do not think carefully about what they put down the drain.
Statements should reflect lesson content.	Personal responses should show thoughtful reflection.

© Harcourt

Name _____

Date _____

Lesson 3—How Can People Conserve Water?

1. Investigation Skill Practice–Identify a Single Independent Variable

Julio planned an experiment where he compared the water used by two homeowners. Both homeowners had similar amounts of property. They lived in the same area of town, so they experienced the same amount of rainfall. However one homeowner had a Xeriscape that included a rock garden, native grasses, and large bushes in his yard. The second homeowner planted a closely trimmed lawn of grass that needed water each week. Julio plans to compare the water bills for both homeowners to find out who uses more water.

What do you think Julio plans to prove by his experiment?
He plans to prove that planting a Xeriscape conserves water.

What is the independent variable in Julio's experiment?
the type of landscaping in the homeowners' yards

2. Reading Focus Skill Practice–Cause and Effect

Read the selection. Describe the cause and effect of Cheryl's actions.

Cheryl walked to the river one day and saw that it had garbage in it. She smelled a bad odor coming from the water, and she noticed that there were no birds or fish near the water. She decided to try to get her town to clean up the river. Cheryl went to the town council meeting to ask them to pass a law about dumping in the river. She organized clean-up days to collect trash from the river. Finally, she wrote letters to the factories along the river to ask them to protect the water in the town. All her efforts paid off. Two years later, the river was clean. It did not smell bad, and there were fish and ducks swimming in it all day.

Cause: Cheryl went to the river and saw garbage, smelled a bad odor, and noticed there were no birds or fish. Effect: She decided to clean it up. She helped pass laws, cleaned up trash, and wrote letters. Effect: The river became clean.

© Harcourt

Name _____

Date _____

Lesson 3—How Can People Conserve Water?

A. Daily Water Usage

We all use water in our daily living. Below is a chart which shows some of the ways we use water and the amounts that we use.

Water Used For	Gallons Used	Water Used For	Gallons Used
bathroom sink	1 per use	kitchen sink	3 per use
clothes washer	30 per load	shower	40 per use
dishwasher	12 per load	toilet	2 per flush

1. Which thing uses the greatest amount of water each time it is used?
shower

2. Arrange the items in the above list from least gallons used each time to the most gallons used each time.
bathroom sink, toilet, kitchen sink, dishwasher, clothes washer, shower

3. Assume you use the toilet 6 times and the bathroom sink 6 times and the shower one time. Complete the table below to find out how many gallons of water a day you might use.

Water Used For	Number of Times	Total Gallons Used
bathroom sink	6	6
shower	1	40
toilet	6	12
Total Used	XXXXXX	58

4. Assume your family does 5 loads of wash in a week and runs the dishwasher two times a day. How many gallons of water is used in one week?
Clothes washer is 5 loads/week x 30 gallons/load = 150 gallons
Dishwasher is 14 loads/week x 12 gallons/load = 168 gallons
Total 318 gallons

Name _____

Science Concepts

3. Circle the substances that can pollute water.

fertilizer   toothpaste   dumped material from mines

food coloring   sewage   milk

pesticides   factory waste

4. Methods of Conserving Water

Explain how each method below helps conserve water resources.

water treatment by factories
Factories treat the water they use in their factory so that it is clean enough to return to the water system.

water reclamation
Water treatment plants recycle used water. It is not clean enough to drink, but it can be used to water plants.

Xeriscaping
People plant their yards with native plants that require less water than grass lawns.

drip irrigation
Farmers drip water onto the soil instead of spraying it on. This allows less evaporation and more water to reach the plants.

Name _____

Date _____

Lesson 1—How Does Uneven Heating of Earth Affect Weather?

A. Explore Word Meanings

Match the clue on the left to the term on the right.

1. __c__ weather

2. __a__ atmosphere

3. __d__ air pressure

4. __e__ convection current

5. __f__ prevailing wind

6. __b__ troposphere

a. The blanket of air surrounding Earth

b. The layer of air closest to Earth's surface

c. The condition of the atmosphere at a certain place and time

d. The weight of the atmosphere pressing down on Earth

e. The upward and downward movement of air in the atmosphere

f. A global wind that blows constantly from the same direction

B. Context Clues

Complete the sentence with the correct word from the box.

air pressure	local wind	stratosphere	prevailing winds

1. The lower __air pressure__ at high altitudes means that the air is thinner and more difficult to breathe.

2. We noticed that the __local wind__ around our lake created a pleasant breeze even on the hottest days.

3. We worry about how our actions on Earth can affect the ozone in the __stratosphere__.

4. The __prevailing winds__ at the equator allowed traders to easily sail across the ocean.

© Harcourt

Name _____

B. Dams

There are many dams that have been built to meet the needs of the people of California. Below is a chart showing information about seven of these dams.

Dam	Year Built	Capacity (acre-ft)
Barrett	1922	44,755
Calaveras	1925	100,000
El Capitan	1934	112,800
Lake Almanor	1927	1,308,000
Nacimiento	1957	350,000
Oroville	1968	3,537,577
San Antonio	1965	350,000

1. What functions do dams in California serve?

The dams provide a storage place for water for use by communities. They also help with flood control and power generation.

2. Rearrange the chart to show the dams from greatest capacity to least capacity.

Dam	Year Built	Capacity (acre-ft)
Oroville	1968	
Lake Almanor	1927	
Nancimiento	1957	
San Antonio	1965	
El Capitan	1934	
Calaveras	1925	
Barrett	1922	

3. What is the total storage capacity of these seven dams?

5,803,132 acre-ft

© Harcourt

© Harcourt

Name _____

Date _____

Lesson 1—How Does Uneven Heating of Earth Affect Weather?

Preview and Question

Identifying main ideas in a lesson and asking questions about them can help you find important information.

- To preview a lesson, read the lesson title and the section titles. Look at the pictures, and read their captions. Try to get an idea of the main topic and think of questions you have about the topic.
- Read to find the answers to your questions. Then recite, or say, the answers aloud. Finally, review what you have read.

As your read this lesson, fill in the chart and practice reading, reciting, and reviewing.

How Does Uneven Heating of Earth Affect Weather?				
Preview	Questions	Read	Recite	Review
The Atmosphere: Weather is the condition of the atmosphere at a certain place and time.	How does the atmosphere change from one place to another?	✓	✓	✓
Preview material should reflect content of the lesson.	Questions should be relevant to the content of the lesson.			

Name _____

Date _____

Lesson 1—How Does Uneven Heating of Earth Affect Weather?

1. Investigation Skill Practice—Predict

Tony decided to ride his bike from his home in New York all the way across the country to Los Angeles. He packed lots of gear and made plans to make plenty of stops. He practiced riding for long distances before he started. But one thing he did not account for was the prevailing westerlies. Those are the winds that usually blow from west to east. How do you predict that the wind will affect his trip from New York to Los Angeles?

During his trip, he will be riding against the wind. It will be a harder

ride than if he rode from Los Angeles to New York. Some local winds

in certain places may make it easier for him to ride.

2. ⭐ Reading Focus Skill Practice—Main Idea and Details

Read the selection. Underline the main idea. Write two details on the lines below.

No one really knows how the city of Chicago got the nickname "The Windy City." Some people think that the city got the name because it is on the edge of Lake Michigan. Wind from the lake blows toward the land because the air over the city heats up and rises. Others believe that the nickname came from Chicago's politicians who are famous for talking so loudly and for so long.

Details: Some people think that the city got the name because it is

on the edge of Lake Michigan. Others think that the nickname came

from Chicago's politicians who are famous for talking so loudly and

for so long.

© Harcourt

Name _____

Date _____

Lesson 2—How Do the Oceans and the Water Cycle Affect Weather?

A. Multiple Meaning Words

Some words can have different meanings depending on the context of the sentence in which they are used. Read the sentence. Circle the correct meaning of the underlined word.

1. As the ships sailed west, the ocean <u>current</u> helped push them along their way.

(stream of water)   taking place in the present day

2. When the water on the <u>surface</u> of the ocean is warm, it evaporates quicker.

(the uppermost layer)   to come up for air

3. The <u>coast</u> of California is affected by ocean water that brings cool weather.

(the area of land near the ocean)   to glide without effort

4. The warm water in the Gulf Stream brings warm temperatures to northern Europe.

a wide impassible gap   (the origin of a major ocean current)

B. Parts of Speech

Choose the correct form of the word to complete the sentence.

1. humidity/humid

Noun: The scientist measured the ___humidity___ by finding the amount of water vapor in the air.

Adjective: She found that the air today is very ___humid___ .

2. precipitation/ precipitate

Noun: The forecaster predicts some form of ___precipitation___ for today.

Verb: We wondered if the clouds would ___precipitate___ during our picnic.

Use with Unit 4.   Science Content Support

© Harcourt

Name _____

Science Concepts

3. Circle the phrase that completes each sentence.

a. Air pressure is greatest _____ .

(at sea level)   at the top of a mountain

b. Most of the Earth's weather occurs in the _____ .

(troposphere)   stratosphere

c. Air pressure pushes air _____ .

downward   (in all directions)

d. _____ air is heavier.

(Cold air)   Warm air

e. The sand is warmer than the water on a sunny day because _____ .

water heats up faster than land   (land heats up faster than water)

f. A sea breeze occurs when _____ .

the wind blows from the sea to the land   the wind blows from the land to the sea

g. The prevailing wind in the United States blows _____ .

(from west to east)   from east to west

h. The sun's rays are more direct _____ .

(at the equator)   in the polar regions

i. Weather in the United States generally moves _____ .

(from California toward the east)   from New York toward the west

j. The wind around the equator is called the _____ .

prevailing westerly   (trade winds)

Science Content Support   (page 2 of 2)   Use with Unit 4.

© Harcourt

Name _____
Date _____

Lesson 2—How Do the Oceans and the Water Cycle Affect Weather?

Skim and Scan

Skimming and scanning are two ways to learn from what you read.

- To skim, quickly read the lesson title and the section titles. Look at the visuals, or images, and read the captions. Use this information to identify the main topics.
- To scan, look quickly through the text for specific details, such as key words or facts.

Before you read this lesson, skim the text to find the main ideas. Then look for key words. If you have questions about a topic, scan the text to find the answers. Fill in the chart below as you skim and scan.

How Do the Oceans and the Water Cycle Affect Weather?	
Skim	**Scan**
Lesson Title: How Do the Oceans and the Water Cycle Affect Weather?	Key Words and Facts: • current • humidity • precipitation • Facts should be accurately excerpted from the text.
Main Idea: The weather of a region is influenced by the ocean and the water cycle.	
Section Titles: The Oceans Affect the Weather, Weather Patterns and the Weather Cycle, Clouds, Precipitation	
Visuals: The Golden Gate Bridge, ocean currents, El Niño photo, the water cycle, heat transfer by the water cycle, types of clouds, How Precipitation Forms.	

Name _____
Date _____

Lesson 2—How Do the Oceans and the Water Cycle Affect Weather?

1. Investigation Skill Practice–Infer

Some factories release steam and hot gasses into the air. Such warm air rises into the atmosphere and warms the colder layers. Based on your knowledge of weather patterns, what can you infer about the effect of hot gasses on the weather of a region?

When hot gasses rise into the atmosphere, they warm the air and allow it to absorb more water vapor than it otherwise could hold. That could cause less rainfall over a region.

2. Reading Focus Skill Practice–Cause and Effect

Read the selection. Describe the cause and effect of the air mass over Siberia.

The Siberian High is a large air mass that stays over Siberia in winter. The air mass forms as snow on the ground, and it cools air over the land. Siberia is so far north that it lacks enough sunlight to melt the snow or to warm the air. The air mass causes great air pressure and cold weather in Siberia and other parts of Asia and Europe.

Cause: Air over the land is cooled and forms the Siberian High air mass during winter. The region does not get enough sunlight to melt snow or warm air. Effect: Cold weather for Siberia and other parts of Asia and Europe.

Name _____

Date _____

Lesson 3—How Is Weather Predicted?

A. Graphic Organizer

Fill in the blanks with the correct word from the box and definition.

barometer	anemometer	hygrometer

Word	Definition	What does it show?
1. barometer	an instrument for measuring air pressure	shows that a low pressure system is coming
2. anemometer	an instrument for measuring wind speed	shows that the wind is blowing at 15 miles per hour
3. hygrometer	an instrument for measuring humidity	shows that the humidity is 85%

B. Context Clues

Complete the sentence with one of the words from the box.

meteorology	meteorologist	front	air mass	forecasted

We watched the ____meteorologist____ on television to find out what the weather will be like tomorrow. She ____forecasted____ that there will be a large, warm ____air mass____ coming toward our area. It will bring humidity and warm days. However, before the warm days are here, the warm air will run into the cold air causing a ____front____ . Thanks to the science of ____meteorology____ we know what the weather will be tomorrow.

Use with Unit 4.   Science Content Support

Name _____

Science Concepts

3. Put the steps in each cycle in the correct sequence. The first step is already completed for you.

A. The Water Cycle

__2__ Water vapor condenses into cloud drops.

__4__ Water soaks into the ground or falls into streams, rivers, lakes, and the oceans.

__1__ Water evaporates from the oceans.

__3__ Water falls to Earth as rain, sleet, snow, or hail.

B. Global Winds

__3__ Cool northern regions receive warm weather when the heat from the tropics is released.

__1__ Water evaporates from the warm water of the tropics.

__2__ Global winds push warm air masses away from the topics.

C. Clouds

__4__ The condensed water forms a cloud.

__1__ Warm air rises.

__3__ Water begins to condense as the air cools.

__2__ As it rises, the warm air cools.

D. Frost

__1__ The ground looses heat more quickly than the air does.

__3__ If the air is cold enough, frost forms.

__2__ As the ground cools, water vapor condenses near the ground.

Science Content Support   (page 2 of 2)   Use with Unit 4.

Lesson Quick Study
Unit 4, Lesson 3

Name _____

Date _____

Lesson 3—How Is Weather Predicted?

1. Investigation Skill Practice—Gather and Record Data

Robert wanted to be a meteorologist. He began by watching the weather in his own region. As he watched the weather and recorded data, he began to notice patterns. He looked for relationships between wind direction and rain, between air pressure and rainfall, and between temperature and air pressure. He even tried to explain what was happening when a weather pattern seemed unusual.

What records do you think Robert kept that helped him make his observations?

He probably recorded air pressure, temperature, wind direction, and

rainfall.

How is gathering and recording data important to learning about weather patterns?

By recording data, you can draw comparisons between similar weather

patterns. You do not have to rely on your memory to make predictions

about how a weather pattern will affect an area.

⭐ Reading Skill Practice—Main Idea and Details

Read the selection. Underline the main idea. Write 3 details on the lines below.

Santa Ana winds are famous for their part in strengthening forest fires. The winds move through the desert and over and through mountains. The air is very warm and dry. The strong winds can turn small forest fires into a huge blaze. Often everything in the path of the fires is destroyed, including forests, homes, and businesses.

Details: The air coming down the mountains is very warm and dry.

The winds can turn a small forest fire into a huge blaze. The fires

destroy forests, homes, and businesses.

Study Skills
Unit 4, Lesson 3

Name _____

Date _____

Lesson 3—How Is Weather Predicted?

Connect Ideas

You can use a web organizer to show how different ideas and information are related.

- List important themes in the ovals in the web's center.
- Add ovals showing main ideas that support each theme.
- Add bubbles for the details that support each main idea.

Complete the web as you read this lesson. Fill in each bubble by adding facts and details. Add your own bubbles as you need them.

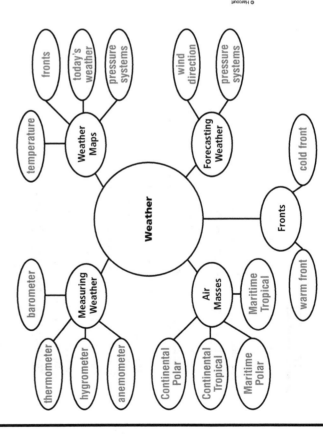

Science Concepts — (left panel)

Name _____

Science Concepts

3. For each scenario, tell what kind of weather might be coming your way.

You notice that the wind in your area has begun to blow from the north.
You may be getting colder weather.

You read your barometer and notice that the air pressure is dropping.
Warm, wet air is coming.

You see large, gray cumulus clouds coming your way.
They could bring rain.

The reading on your hygrometer shows a rapid increase in humidity.
You could get rain.

The weather map shows that the area west of you has snow storms and the wind direction is blowing east.
You may get the snow storm from the west.

A cold front is coming quickly to your area where you now have warm humid weather.
You will get rain with possible thunderstorms. Following that will be cool days.

Today you have cold weather but a warm front is coming.
You may get rain or a storm that could last many hours. This will be followed by warmer weather.

Your area is getting a continental polar air mass.
You will get cold dry weather.

A maritime tropical air mass is predicted for your region.
You will have warm, humid weather.

© Harcourt

Right panel

Name _____

Date _____

Lesson 3—How Is Weather Predicted?

A. Reading Weather Maps

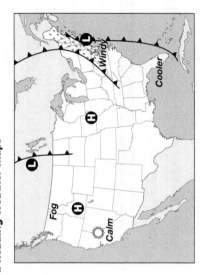

Use the weather map shown above to answer the following questions.

1. What is the weather like in California?
   Calm

2. Which part of the United States is experiencing windy conditions?
   the northeastern part

3. What does the letter "H" stand for on the map?
   high pressure system

4. Name one state that is experiencing fog according to the map.
   Washington, Idaho, or Montana

© Harcourt

Name _____

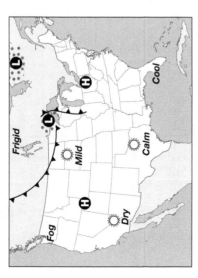

Use the weather map above to answer the following questions.

1. What type of pressure system is in Ohio?
   a high pressure system

2. What type of front is moving through Wisconsin and northern Illinois?
   warm front

3. Describe which part of the country a warm front is moving through.
   parts of Canada, Wisconsin, Michigan, and northern Illinois

4. Describe which part of the country a cold front is moving through.
   northern U.S. in Minnesota and North Dakota

Name _____

B. Creating Weather Maps

Use the United States map shown above to complete the exercises described below.

1. Create a weather map using the map above with the following characteristics:
   - High pressure systems in the Utah/Nevada area and in the New York area.
   - Low pressure system in Iowa
   - A cold front that goes from Ohio to Georgia
   - A warm front in the California/Nevada area

   Drawing should reflect the characteristics described above with use of the appropriate symbols

Name _____

Date _____

Lesson 4—What Are the Causes and Effects of Severe Weather?

A. Work Origin/Etymology

Choose one word from the box that is derived from the word given. Write the word and its definition in the table.

monsoon	hurricane	thunderstorm	tornado

Word	Derived From	Language of Origin	Definition
hurricane	*huracan*	Spanish	a large, rotating tropical storm system with wind speeds of at least 119 km/hr (74 mi/hr)
monsoon	*mawsim*	Arabic	a large wind system that reverses direction seasonally
tornado	*tronada*	Spanish	a violently spinning column of air that touches the ground
thunderstorm	*thunor*	Old English	a strong storm with rain, lightning, and thunder

B. Write a sentence for each word listed.

monsoon _____

Sentences should use vocabulary word accurately.

hurricane _____

tornado _____

© Harcourt

Use with Unit 4.   Science Content Support   **CS 111**

Name _____

C. Interpreting Weather Maps

Use the weather map above to answer the following questions.

1. Name a state that is receiving rain.
   Nevada, California, Florida

2. What is the weather like in Dallas, Texas?
   partly sunny, partly cloudy, with a temperature of 47 degrees F

3. What is the weather like in northwestern Ohio and Northeastern Indiana?
   a mixture of snow and rain

4. Name one part of the country that has sunny weather.
   Oklahoma, Idaho

5. What type of weather is usually experienced in a high-pressure area?
   fair

6. What type of weather is usually experienced in a low-pressure area?
   stormy

© Harcourt

CS 110   Science Content Support   (page 4 of 4)   Use with Unit 4.

Name _____

Date _____

Lesson 4—What Are the Causes and Effects of Severe Weather?

Write to Learn

Writing about what you read can help you better understand and remember information.

- Writing down the information that you learn from each lesson leads you to think about the information.
- Writing your own response to the new information makes it more meaningful to you.

As you read the lesson, pay attention to new and important information. Keep track of the information and your responses in the log below.

What Are the Causes and Effects of Severe Weather?	
What I Learned	**Personal Response**
The monsoons are a seasonal event caused by a shift in wind direction.	Wet, humid, rainy days flow one to another endlessly, until they end and go away as if they had never been here at all.
Statements should reflect lesson content.	Personal responses should show thoughtful reflection.

Name _____

Date _____

Lesson 4—What Are the Causes and Effects of Severe Weather?

1. Investigation Skill Practice—Predict

When you hear the National Weather Service announce that a hurricane is on the way for your area, you must make certain preparations. Based on what you know about severe weather, what can you predict will happen when the hurricane arrives?

I can predict that there will be high winds, heavy rain, and storm surges near the ocean.

How would your prediction of the conditions be different if the weather service had announced a thunderstorm for your area?

For a thunderstorm, I would predict rain, lightening, and thunder lasting a short time.

2. Reading Skill Practice—Cause and Effect

Read the selection. Describe the cause and effect of a storm surge.

A storm surge is a flow of ocean water that rises during a hurricane. It is caused by strong winds that push water ahead of the storm. A storm surge can cause more damage than the hurricane's high winds or rain. That's because water is extremely heavy. It moves with great power and can smash buildings and vehicles. It can push houses over, knock trees down, and carry cars away. In addition, the water often carries heavy debris. When the storm surge recedes, it leaves mountains of branches, broken equipment, and dirt. Such debris is difficult and expensive to remove.

Cause: Storm surge is caused by the strong winds pushing water ahead of the storm. Effect: Surges can cause more damage than wind or rain by pushing houses over, knocking trees down, and carrying cars away. It also leaves mountains of debris that must be moved.

Name _____

Date _____

Lesson 1—What Is the Sun?

| star |
| sun |
| fusion |

A. Analogies

An analogy is made of two pairs of words. The words in each pair are related in the same way. Think about the relationships of the following pairs of words. Then choose a word from the box to complete the analogy.

1. *Sun* is to *day* as ____ **star** ____ is to *night*.

2. ____ **Fusion** ____ is to *star* as *wood* is to *fire*.

3. *Water* is to *hydroelectric dam* as ____ **sun** ____ is to *solar panel*.

B. Categorizing and Classifying

In each group below, one word does not belong to the same category as the others. Circle the letter of that word. Then classify the remaining words by writing a label for that group.

1. A. sun
   B. moon
   C. planets
   Ⓓ fusion

   ____ members of the solar system

2. A. color
   Ⓑ number of planets
   C. distance from Earth
   D. size

   ____ ways of classifying stars

3. A. X rays
   B. visible light
   Ⓒ fusion
   D. radio waves

   ____ types of energy from the sun

Use with Unit 5.

© Harcourt

Name _____

Science Concepts

3. Fill in the chart with accurate information about each type of storm.

	tornado	thunderstorm	monsoon	hurricane	typhoon
duration of storm	minutes to hours	less than one hour	a season, months	a week	a week
size of storm	very narrow path	covers a region but not huge	covers large region	485 km (300 miles) across	485 km (300 miles) across
cause of storm damage	flying debris	lightning, wind, hail	heavy rain	high winds, storm surge	high winds, storm surge
causes of storm	funnel of low pressure air reaches from storm cloud	forms when warm air moves upward rapidly	sea breeze causes air to rise, cool, and produce rain	warm, wet winds rotate around low pressure system over the ocean	warm, wet winds rotate around low pressure system over the ocean
predictability	poor	good	excellent	Good	good

4. Answer the questions.

What is the difference between a hurricane and a typhoon?

A hurricane forms over the North Atlantic Ocean, the North Pacific Ocean (east of the International Date Line), and the South Pacific Ocean (east of 160°E). A typhoon is a similar storm that forms in the North Pacific west of the International Date Line.

What is the eye of a hurricane?

The eye of a hurricane is a calm center, caused by dry, cool air being pulled down from above. Around the eye is the eye wall, the most intense part of the storm.

© Harcourt

Name _____

Date _____

Lesson 1—What Is the Sun?

1. Investigation Skill Practice—Predict

Solar power relies on sunny days, long summers, and short winters. Panels collect the sun's energy and transformers change it into electricity. However, solar energy is not practical all the time. When the sun does not shine, the system cannot collect the sun's energy. In addition, solar panels and the equipment it requires are expensive to install. It is difficult to install a solar heating system in a house that has already been built.

Make predictions to answer the following questions.

Where do you think solar panel systems might sell the best and the worst?
They might sell the best in mild climates with long summers and sunny days. They would sell the worst in cold, northern regions with long winters and short days.

Do you predict that solar heating will become popular throughout the nation? Tell why or why not.
No, because the system is expensive and difficult to install on existing homes. It is also not ideal for cold, northern regions.

2. Reading Skill Practice—Main Idea and Details

Read the selection. Underline the main idea. Write two details on the lines below.

Icarus and Daedalus are mythical characters who are known for their unsuccessful flight toward the sun. Daedalus built wings for himself and his son so they could leave the island of Crete. He fastened feathers to the wings with wax. Then the two flew away from the island. However, his son, Icarus, flew too close to the sun. The sun's warmth melted the wax on his wings, and he fell to his death in the sea.

Daedalus built wings and fastened feathers with wax. Icarus flew too close to the sun and the wax melted, making him fall to his death in the sea.

© Harcourt

Use with Unit 5.   (page 1 of 2)   Science Content Support   **CS 117**

Name _____

Date _____

Lesson 1—What Is the Sun?

Anticipation Guide

An anticipation guide can help you anticipate, or predict, what you will learn as you read.

• Look at the section titles for clues.
• Preview the Reading Check question at the end of each section. Use what you know about the subject of each section to predict the answers.
• Read to find out whether your predictions were correct.

As you read the section, complete your own anticipation guide below. Predict answers to each question and check to see if your predictions were correct.

What Is the Sun?		
Stars		
Reading Check	Prediction	Correct?
What are two ways that scientists classify stars?	In this section, we will learn about different types of stars.	✓

Features of the Sun		
Reading Check	Prediction	Correct?
What are the layers of the sun?	In this section we will learn that the sun is not simply a big ball of gas.	✓

How the Sun Produces Energy		
Reading Check	Prediction	Correct?
How does the sun produce energy?	In this section we will learn about the types of energy that comes from the sun and how it is used on Earth.	✓

© Harcourt

CS 116 Science Content Support   Use with Unit 5.

Name

Date

Lesson 2—What Makes Up the Solar System?

A. Context Clues

Complete the sentence with the correct word from the box.

| comet |
| meteors |
| planet |
| satellite |
| solar system |

Ida dreams of traveling through space and seeing all the objects of the __solar system__. She hopes to see the __planets__ including Jupiter, Saturn, and Venus. She is interested in Jupiter because of its many __satellites__. She wonders what it would be like to live in a place with so many moons. Ida hopes that her dream of space travel would come true someday. In the meantime, she observes the sky on her own. She looks for __comets__ that appear at intervals of many years. She tracks __meteors__ that enter the earth's atmosphere as shooting stars. She also studies hard at school to learn all she can about science and space.

B. Matching

Write the letter of the definition from the right next the correct word on the left.

1. __e__ comet
2. __a__ solar system
3. __d__ asteroid
4. __c__ satellite
5. __b__ planet

a. a star and all the planets and other objects that revolve around it

b. a body that revolves around a star

c. a body in space that orbits a larger body

d. a piece of rock and metal that orbits the sun, forming a belt between Mars and Jupiter

e. a ball of ice, rock, and frozen gases that orbits the sun

Use with Unit 5.

Science Content Support CS 119

© Harcourt

Name

Science Concepts

3. Match the description with one of the words from the box.

| photosphere |
| core |
| radiation zone |
| convection zone |

a. where sunspots appear __photosphere__

b. produces solar flares __photosphere__

c. sits at the center of the sun __core__

d. contains most of the sun's mass __core__

e. energy passes through zone toward surface __radiation zone__

f. the area that can be seen on Earth __photosphere__

g. sun's outer zone __convection zone__

4. Answer the questions about the sun.

Is it the brightest star? __no__

Is it the hottest star? __no__

Is it the biggest star? __no__

Is it the largest object in the solar system? __yes__

Is it the closest star to Earth? __yes__

5. Answer the questions about fusion.

What happens during fusion?

__The nuclei of two hydrogen atoms fuse and release energy.__

What kinds of waves come from the sun?

__Electromagnetic waves include visible light, X rays, radio waves, and ultraviolet rays.__

CS 118 Science Content Support (page 2 of 2) Use with Unit 5.

© Harcourt

Name _____

Date _____

Lesson 2—What Makes Up the Solar System?

Pose Questions

Posing, or asking questions, as you read can help you understand what you are reading.

- Form questions as you read. For example, you may ask how a science concept is connected to other concepts.
- Use the questions to guide your reading. Look for answers as you read.

Before you read this lesson, write a list of questions in the chart below. Look for the answers as you read. Record the answers in the chart.

What Makes Up the Solar System?	
Questions	Answers
What separates the inner planets from the outer planets?	The asteroid belt between Mars and Jupiter divides the inner planets from the outer planets.
Questions should be relevant to lesson content.	Answers should accurately answer question.

© Harcourt

Name _____

Date _____

Lesson 2—What Makes Up the Solar System?

1. Investigation Skill Practice—Infer

Many of the brightest stars and galaxies in the sky have Arabic names, such as Rigel, Aldebaran, Vega, Deneb, Shedir, and Betelgeuse. They were named very long ago. However, some stars that are not very bright are unnamed. They are designated only by their telescopic coordinates.

Make inferences to explain why many bright stars have Arabic names.

Long ago the people in Arabian peninsula observed bright stars in the sky and gave them their own names. We use many of these names for stars today.

Make inferences to explain why dim stars have no names.

Dim stars are hard to see, and there are so many of them that it would be impossible to have a name for every one.

2. Reading Skill Practice—Main Idea and Details

Read the selection. Underline the main idea. Write three details on the lines below.

Edmond Halley first figured out that a streak in the sky was a comet that moves around the sun every 76 years. He did this by watching the sky and by doing research about comets throughout history. He found out that every 76 years people reported a bright streak in the sky. No one could explain it, but Halley determined that these reports must have referred to the same comet. His research and attention to history helped him discover the truth about a mysterious comet that bears his name today.

Details: Halley watched the sky. He did research about comets throughout history. He determined that the reports must refer to the same comet.

_____

_____

_____

© Harcourt

Name _____

Date _____

Lesson 2—What Makes Up the Solar System?

A. Space Research/Exploration—Internet Research

Visit the NASA government website at *http://www.nasa.gov* Click on the *Missions* button. Select one of the *Current Missions* listed on the website. Click on the icon for that mission and read about it. Use the information you read to answer the questions below.

1. What is the name of the mission?
_____

2. When does the mission begin and end?
_____

3. Describe the purpose of the mission.
_____
_____

4. Is the mission manned or unmanned?
_____

5. What parts of the solar system will be explored during this mission?
_____
_____

Answers will vary. Check the website for answers to the questions above concerning the mission the student has chosen.

© Harcourt

Name _____

Science Concepts

3. Answer the questions below about the planets.

What are the planets of the solar system?
Mercury, Venus, Earth, Mars, Jupiter, Saturn, Neptune, Uranus, and Pluto

Which planets are gas giants?
Jupiter, Saturn, Neptune, and Uranus

Which are the inner planets?
Mercury, Venus, Earth, and Mars.

What divides the planets into inner planets and outer planets?
the asteroid belt

Why do some people argue that Pluto is not really a planet?
Because it is small and rocky, it has a satellite that is almost the same size as the planet, and its orbit is unusual.

4. Answer the questions below about asteroids.

How big is an asteroid?
smaller than 621 miles in diameter

Where are most asteroids found?
in the asteroid belt between Jupiter and Mars

5. Answer the questions below about comets.

What does a comet look like?
When it is visible to Earth, it looks like a long streak of light

When can you see a comet?
Comets come in regular intervals. Halley's comet comes every 76 years.

How is a comet different from a star?
It orbits the sun.

How is a comet different from a planet?
It is much smaller than a planet.

© Harcourt

Name _____

Name _____

Date _____

Lesson 3—What Holds the Moon and Planets in Place?

A. Context Clues

Read the sentences. Use the context clues to help you choose the correct meaning of the underlined word. Circle its meaning. Look up the word in a glossary if you need help.

1. The orbit of Pluto is unusual because it crosses Neptune's orbit, making it come closer to the sun during some periods and farther away in other periods.

   the path something takes as it revolves around another body
   oval-shaped
   the attraction between all objects

2. The planets' path around the sun is not circular, it is elliptical.

   long
   inconsistent
   (oval-shaped)

3. The car's inertia as it skidded on wet ice made it difficult to stop.

   slippery tires
   (tendency to keep moving)
   bad breaks

4. When you throw a ball in the air, Earth's gravity brings the ball back to the ground.

   (attraction between all objects in the universe)
   orbit
   oxygen content

5. The star was so small that it could only be seen through a telescope.

   an instrument to see very small things
   an instrument to measure air pressure
   (an instrument to see things far away)

Use with Unit 5.

Name _____

B. Space Research/Exploration—Research Halley's Comet

Use the library or internet to research Halley's Comet. Answer the questions below.

1. What causes the tail on Halley's Comet?

   The comet is made of ice, which melts, leaving a trail of gas.

2. Why does Halley's Comet travel through our solar system regularly?

   It orbits the sun.

3. Which direction does a comet's tail point?

   Comets can have two tails. One tail always points away from the sun.

4. When is the next time we will be able to see Halley's Comet?

   2061–2062

5. Who is the comet named after?

   Edmond Halley

6. Write a short paragraph explaining how people have observed Halley's Comet since 1682?

   In the 1682, Edmond Halley was the first person to realize that this comet was the very same one that others observed in 1531 and 1607. When the comet returned in 1835, they recorded their observations. In 1910, Halley's Comet was photographed. In 1985 and 1986 scientists called astronomers were able to observe the comet from both the ground and space.

7. The center of Halley's Comet is called the nucleus. Write three sentences explaining this comet's nucleus.

   The nucleus is very dark. This actually makes it one of the darkest things in the solar system. It is 16 × 8 × 8 kilometers.

Lesson 3—What Holds the Moon and Planets in Place?

1 Investigation Skill Practice—Model

Glen made a model to help him understand the phases of the moon. He sat in a dark room with a flashlight and a white softball. He put the flashlight on a table and shined it on the ball. Then he held the ball making the light reflect from the surface. He held the ball so that he could see one entire side of the ball lit up. Then he moved it again so that he could see only half of the ball lit up. Finally, he held the ball so that the ball appeared to be completely in shadow except for a tiny sliver of light on one side.

What did the flashlight represent in Glen's model?

the sun

What did the ball represent?

the moon

How did his model help explain the phases of the moon?

By moving the ball, he could understand how the shadow from the sun and

the reflected light could appear to people on Earth as a changing phase.

2. Reading Focus Skill Practice—Cause and Effect

Read the selection. Describe the cause and effect relationships.

All objects with mass in the solar system have their own gravitational pull. For example, the gravity of the sun pulls on the Earth. The gravity of Earth pulls on the moon. The moon also has its own gravitational force. We can tell that this is true because the gravity of the moon pulls on the ocean water on Earth. This pull toward the moon is what creates high tide and low tide all over the world.

Cause: Gravity causes the sun to pull on the Earth and the Earth to pull

on the moon and the moon to pull on the ocean water. Effect: The pull of

the moon's gravity creates ocean tides on Earth.

Use with Unit 5.   (page 1 of 2)   Science Content Support   CS 127

© Harcourt

Lesson 3—What Holds the Moon and Planets in Place?

Take Notes

Taking notes can help you remember important ideas.

- Write down important facts and ideas. Use your own words. You do not have to write in complete sentences.
- One way to organize notes is in a chart. Write down the main ideas in one column and facts and details in another.

As you read this lesson, use the chart below to take notes.

What Holds the Moon and Planets in Place?	
Main Ideas	**Facts**
• Ptolemy believed the sun revolved around the Earth.	• Ptolemy's model was wrong.
• Students' main ideas should reflect content of lesson.	**Students' facts should support the main ideas.**
•	•
•	•
•	•
•	•

CS 126   Science Content Support   Use with Unit 5.

© Harcourt

Name _____

Science Concepts

3. **A myth is not based on truth. Explain why these myths are untrue.**

Myth 1: The moon, sun, and planets revolve around the Earth.
The earth and planets revolve around the sun. The moon revolves
around the Earth and sun.
_____
_____

Myth 2: The planets move in circular orbits around the sun.
The planets' orbits are slightly elliptical, not circular.
_____
_____

Myth 3: The Earth will one day fall into the sun.
It will not fall into the sun, because its inertia to continue in a straight
line is equal to the gravitational pull on it to orbit around the sun.
_____
_____

Myth 4: The moon changes shape every night, which is why it always looks
different.
The moon looks like it changes shape because it moves in relation to
Earth, allowing different amounts of the sun's reflection to be visible
on Earth.
_____

Myth 5: Astronauts are weightless because there is no air in space.
Astronauts are weightless because inertia and gravity are equally
balanced as they orbit Earth.
_____

absorb

acid

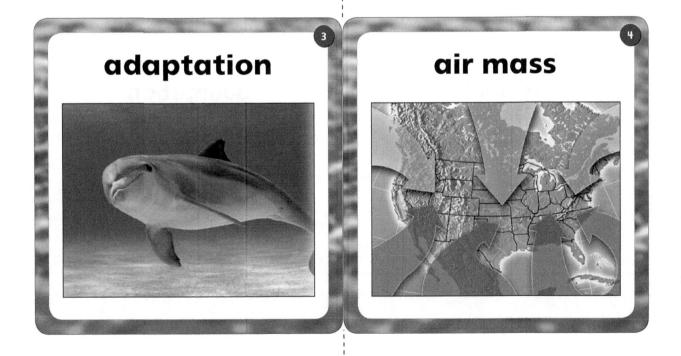

adaptation

air mass

acid

[AS•id]

A chemical compound that turns blue litmus paper red and has a pH of less than 7.

The juice from an orange is a mild acid.

absorb

[ab•ZAWRB]

To take in.

Sponges absorb liquid easily.

air mass

[AIR MAS]

A large body of air that has similar temperature and humidity throughout.

The blue arrows represent cool air masses.

adaptation

[ad•uhp•TAY•shuhn]

A trait or characteristic that helps an organism survive.

The dolphin's flippers are an adaptation that helps it swim.

air pressure

alloy

anemometer

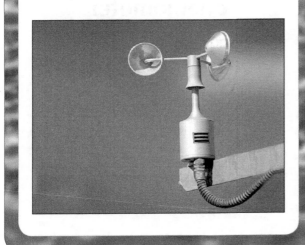

aqueduct

© Harcourt

alloy

[AL•OY]

A solid solution in which a metal or a nonmetal dissolves in a metal.

This statue is made of an *alloy* called bronze.

6

air pressure

[air PRESH•er]

The weight of the atmosphere pressing down on Earth.

Air pressure changes with altitude.

5

aqueduct

[AK•wuh•duhkt]

A pipe or channel that is used to transport water.

You can see *aqueducts* built by ancient Romans throughout western Europe.

8

anemometer

[an•uh•MAHM•uht•er]

An instrument for measuring wind speed.

Wind makes an *anemometer* spin.

7

array

artery

asteroid

atmosphere

artery

[ART•er•ee]

A blood vessel that carries blood from the heart to the rest of the body.

Arteries (red) carry blood from the heart to the body.

10

array

[uh•RAY]

A pattern of atoms.

This *array* of atoms can be seen only through a very powerful microscope.

9

atmosphere

[AT•muhs•fir]

The blanket of air surrounding Earth.

Earth's *atmosphere* has several layers.

12

asteroid

[AS•ter•oyd]

A piece of rock and metal that orbits the sun.

Some *asteroids* are pieces of rock from collisions of larger objects in space.

11

atom
13

atomic number
14

6
C
Carbon

balance
15

barometer
16

atomic number

[uh·TAHM·ik NUHM·ber]

The number of protons in an atom.

The *atomic number* of carbon is 6.

14

atom

[AT·uhm]

The smallest unit of an element, that has the properties of that element.

Nearly all *atoms* have neutrons.

13

barometer

[buh·RAHM·uht·er]

An instrument for measuring air pressure.

The original *barometer* used mercury in a glass tube to measure air pressure.

16

balance

[BAL·uhns]

A tool that measures an object's mass.

The *balance* shows that the masses of these objects are equal.

15

barometric pressure

17

base

18

binoculars

19

bladder

20

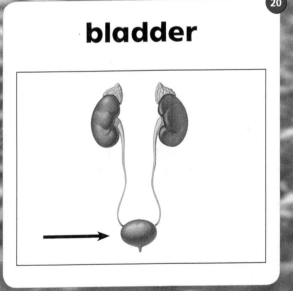

base

[BAYS]

A chemical compound that turns red litmus paper blue and has a pH of more than 7.

Soap is a mild *base*.

18

barometric pressure

[bair•uh•MEH•trik PRESH•er]

The weight of the atmosphere pressing down on Earth; also called air pressure.

When the *barometric pressure* drops quickly, you can expect a storm.

17

bladder

[BLAD•er]

A saclike muscular organ where urine is stored until it is released from the body.

The *bladder* is connected to the kidneys.

20

binoculars

[by•NAHK•yuh•lerz]

A device for looking at distant object that magnifies what is seen using a lens for each eye.

You can use *binoculars* to see things that are far away.

19

© Harcourt

blizzard

blood circulation

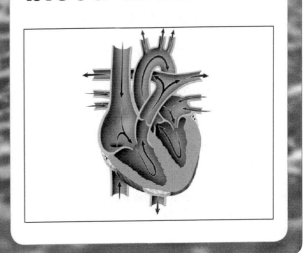

boil

brittle

blood circulation

[BLUHD ser•kyoo•LAY•shuhn]

The movement of blood through the body, taking oxygen and nutrients to the cells and wastes away from the cells.

The heart provides the force for *blood circulation*.

22

blizzard

[BLIZ•erd]

A severe snowstorm.

It is hard to see in a *blizzard*.

21

brittle

[BRIT•uhl]

Able to be broken or crushed easily.

Chalk is *brittle*.

24

boil

[BOYL]

When a substance changes from a liquid to a gas.

Water *boils* at 100°C (212°F).

23

capillary

25

carbon dioxide

26

cardiovascular

27

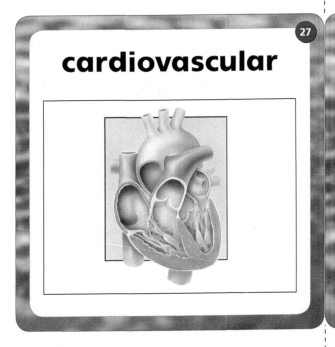

cell

28

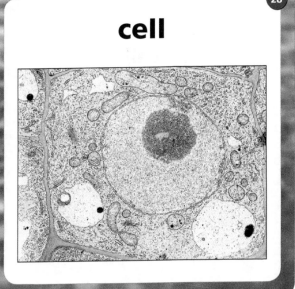

carbon dioxide

[KAR•buhn dy•AHK•syd]

A molecule formed from one atom of carbon and two atoms of oxygen.

Carbon dioxide is the compound in dry ice.

26

capillary

[KAP•uh•lair•ee]

One of tiny blood vessels that exchange materials between the blood and body cells.

You have many *capillaries* in your skin.

25

cell

[sel]

The basic unit of structure and function of all living things.

Plants *cells* have a cell wall.

28

cardiovascular

[kar•dee•oh•VAS•kyoo•ler]

Having to do with the heart and the circulatory system.

The condition of your heart is important to your *cardiovascular* health.

27

cellular respiration

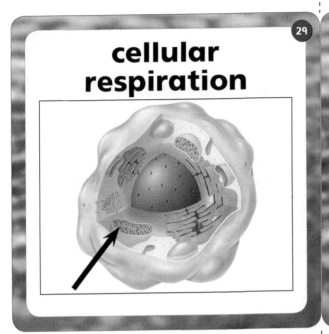

cellular waste

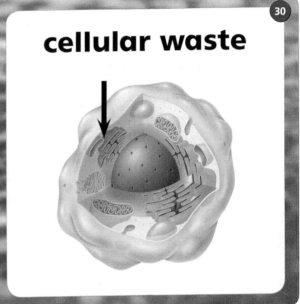

chaos theory

chemical change

© Harcourt

cellular waste

[SEL•yoo•ler WAYST]

The product of cell functions.

Vesicles store cellular waste.

cellular respiration

[SEL•yoo•ler res•puh•RAY•shuhn]

The process by which cells use oxygen to break down sugar to release energy.

Cellular respiration takes place in the mitochondria.

chemical change

[KEM•ih•kuhl CHAYNJ]

A change in which a substance or two becomes a new substance or two.

Burning is one kind of *chemical change*.

chaos theory

[KAY•ahs THEE•uh•ree]

The idea that very small changes can have major effects on a system.

An illustration of *chaos theory* is the effect that one falling domino has on the others in a row.

chemical compound

33

chemical property

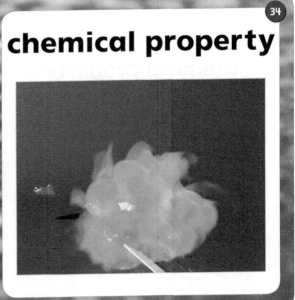

34

chemical reaction

35

chlorophyll

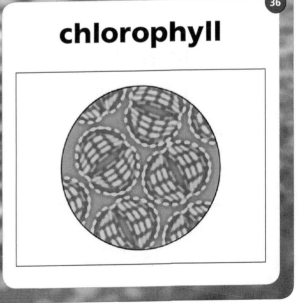

36

© Harcourt

chemical property

[KEM•ih•kuhl PRAHP•er•tee]

A property that involves the ability of a substance to react with other materials and form new substances.

Flammability is one kind of *chemical property*.

chemical compound

[KEM•ih•kuhl KAHM•pownd]

A substance made of two or more different elements.

Water is a *chemical compound* because it is made of hydrogen and oxygen.

chlorophyll

[KLAWR•uh•fil]

A green pigment that allows a plant cell to use light to make food.

Chlorophyll is what makes leaves green.

chemical reaction

[KEM•ih•kuhl ree•AK•shuhn]

A change in which one or more new substances are formed.

Rusting is one kind of *chemical reaction*.

circulation

37

circulatory system

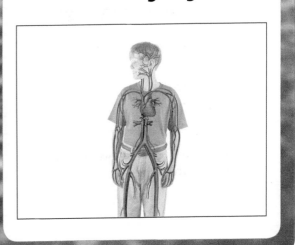

38

classify

39

cloud

40

circulatory system

[SER•kyoo•luh•tawr•ee SIS•tuhm]

A group of organs that transports needed materials throughout the body.

The *circulatory system* moves blood throughout the body.

38

circulation

[ser•kyoo•LAY•shuhn]

The movement of something from place to place (water and air around Earth).

The water cycle is the *circulation* of water from the atmosphere to Earth's surface and back to the atmosphere.

37

cloud

[KLOWD]

Water that has either condensed on dust particles in the air, or frozen at a high altitude.

The types of *clouds* are related to different kinds of weather.

40

classify

[KLAS•uh•fy]

To group or organize objects or events into categories based on similar criteria.

This student is *classifying* objects.

39

© Harcourt

colon

comet

compound

Vinegar

Baking Soda

conclusion

42

comet

[KAHM•it]

A ball of ice, rock, and frozen gases that orbits the sun.

A *comet's* orbit around the sun is usually irregular.

41

colon

[KOH•luhn]

An organ that stores solid waste until it is released from the body.

The *colon* is part of the digestive system.

44

conclusion

[kuhn•KLOO•zhuhn]

A decision you make based on information.

These students are using information from an experiment to draw a *conclusion*.

43

compound

[KAHM•pownd]

A substance made of two or more different elements.

Baking soda and vinegar are *compounds*.

© Harcourt

condensation

45

conductivity

46

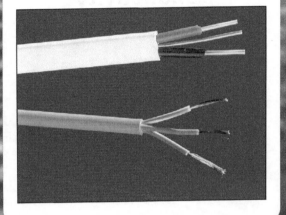

conservation

47

TOWN WATER INTAKE
PLEASE DO NOT WASH
VEHICLES HERE.

control variable

48

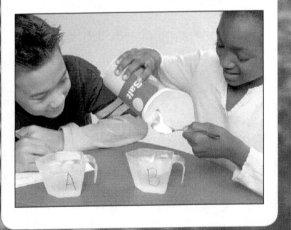

conductivity

[kahn•duhk•TIV•uh•tee]

The ability of a metal to transfer energy easily.

These wires are made of metal that has very high *conductivity*.

46

condensation

[kahn•duhn•SAY•shuhn]

The process by which a gas changes into a liquid.

Rain results from *condensation*.

45

control variable

[kuhn•TROHL VAIR•ee•uh•buhl]

The parts of an investigation that you can control.

It is important to keep track of your *control variables*.

48

conservation

[kahn•ser•VAY•shuhn]

The preserving and protecting of a resource.

Protecting resources is a part of *conservation*.

47

© Harcourt

convection

49

convection currents

50

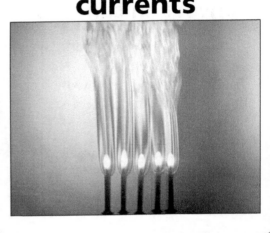

creek

51

crescent moon

52

convection currents

[kuhn•VEK•shuhn KER•uhnts]

The upward and downward movements of a gas or a liquid.

These candles heat the air and cause it to move in a *convection current*.

convection

[kuhn•VEK•shuhn]

Circular movement in a liquid or gas, resulting from regions of different temperatures and different densities.

Convection in the atmosphere produces rain clouds.

crescent moon

[KRES•uhnt moon]

The moon phase just after or just before a new moon.

There are two *crescent moons* in a month.

creek

[KREEK]

A narrow and shallow river.

Water can move quickly, even in a small *creek*.

criteria

53

current

54

cyclone

55

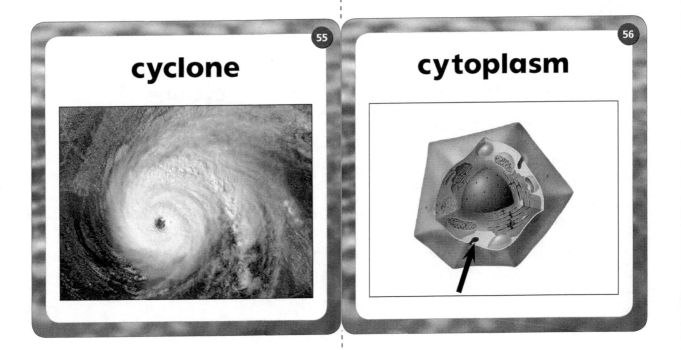

cytoplasm

56

current

[KER•uhnt]

A stream of water that flows like a river through the ocean.

Ocean *currents* flow in only one direction.

criteria

[kry•TIR•ee•uh]

The specific qualities that allow you to group items.

The students are classifying the objects according to the *criteria* they discussed.

cytoplasm

[SYT•oh•plaz•uhm]

A jellylike substance in a cell between the cell membrane and the nucleus, containing most organelles.

Cytoplasm helps protect organelles.

cyclone

[SY•klohn]

A rapidly turning air mass.

The air in a *cyclone* turns counterclockwise in the Northern Hemisphere.

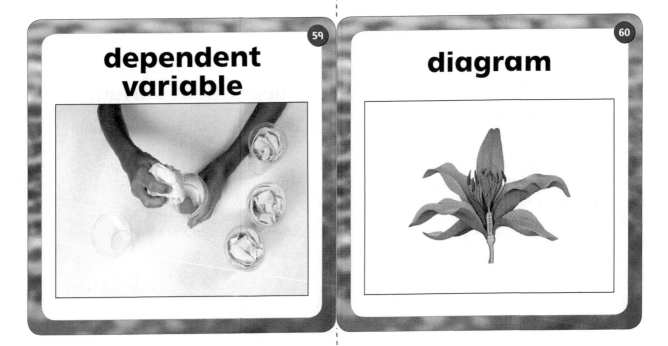

dam 57

deflect 58

dependent variable 59

diagram 60

deflect

[dee•FLEKT]

To turn something from its path, as when winds are deflected by a moutain range.

The windshield of a car *deflects* the air.

dam

[DAM]

A barrier across a river, controlling its flow.

Dams can be natural, animal-made, or human-made.

diagram

[DY•uh•gram]

A drawing, sketch, or other visual representation that explains an idea or object.

This *diagram* shows the parts of a flower.

dependent variable

[dee•PEN•duhnt VAIR•ee•uh•buhl]

The part of an investigation that is out of your control.

The results of your investigation are shown by a *dependent variable*.

© Harcourt

diffusion

61

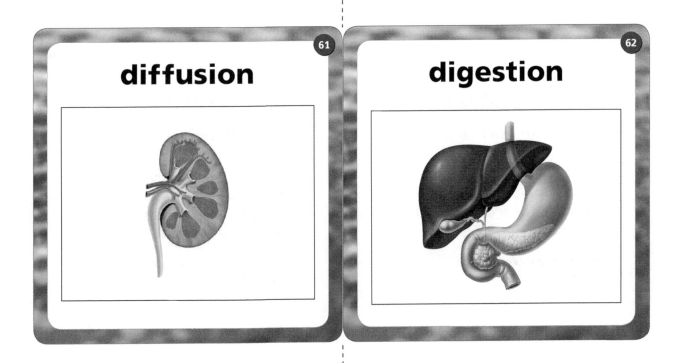

digestion

62

digestive system

63

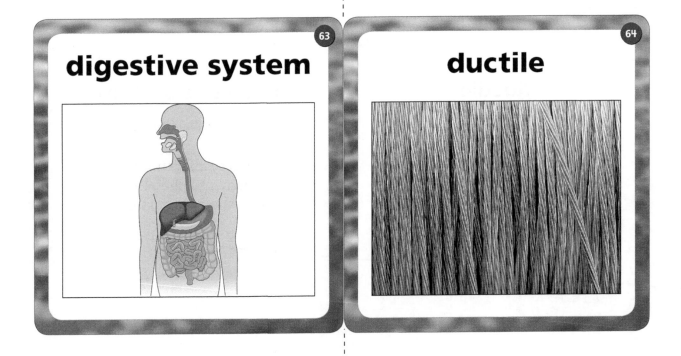

ductile

64

digestion

[dih•JES•chuhn]

The process of breaking food down into nutrients the body's cells need for energy, growth, and repair.

Several organs are involved in *digestion*.

62

diffusion

[dih•FYOO•zhuhn]

The movement of materials from an area of higher concentration to an area of lower concentration.

Nephrons in the kidneys remove liquid waste through *diffusion*.

61

ductile

[DUHK•tuhl]

Able to be pulled into thin strands.

Ductile metal is used to make wire.

64

digestive system

[dih•JES•tive SIS•tuhm]

The organ system that breaks food down into chemical nutrients the body can use.

The *digestive system* includes the stomach and the intestines.

63

Earth

65

El Niño

66

electrical conductivity

67

electron

68

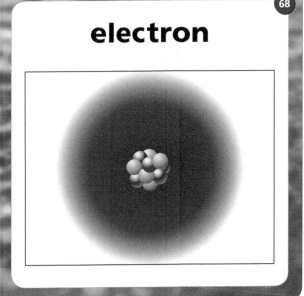

El Niño

[el NEEN•yoh]

Warming of South American equatorial ocean waters that leads to changing weather patterns.

On this satellite map, you can see the warm water that causes *el Niño*.

66

Earth

[ERTH]

The planet we live on.

Earth looks mostly blue from space.

65

electron

[ee•LEK•trahn]

One of the particles in an atom.

An *electron* has a negative charge.

68

electrical conductivity

[ee•LEK•trih•kuhl
kahn•duhk•TIV•uh•tee]

The ability of a metal to transfer electrons.

Silver has *electrical conductivity*.

67

© Harcourt

electron microscope

69

element

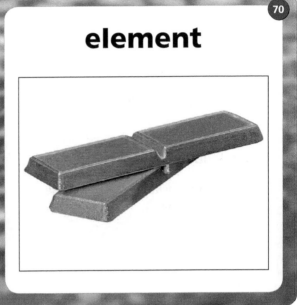

70

elliptical

71

Equator

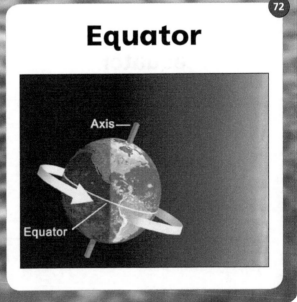

Axis

Equator

72

element

[EL•uh•muhnt]

A substance made up of only
one kind of atom.

Gold is an *element* because it is made
of only gold atoms.

70

electron microscope

[ee•LEK•trahn MY•kruh•skohp]

A microscope that uses a
stream of electrons to produce
images of objects.

The *electron microscope* is very
powerful.

69

equator

[ee•KWAYT•er]

An imaginary line around Earth
equally distant from the North
and South Poles.

The *equator* divides Earth into the
Northern and Southern Hemispheres.

72

elliptical

[eh•LIP•tuh•kuhl]

Oval shaped.

The orbits of most planets are *elliptical*.

71

erosion

73

esophagus

74

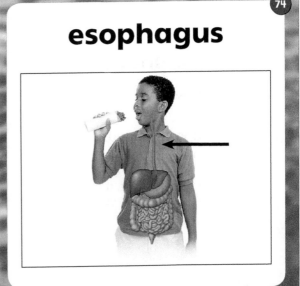

evaporate

75

evaporation

76

© Harcourt

esophagus

[ih•SAHF•uh•guhs]

A long tube that leads from the mouth to the stomach.

When you swallow food, it moves down your *esophagus* to your stomach.

74

erosion

[ee•ROH•zhuhn]

The process of moving sediment by wind, moving water, or ice.

This gully was formed by *erosion*.

73

evaporation

[ee•vap•uh•RAY•shuhn]

The process by which liquid changes into a gas.

The water level of this lake has dropped because of *evaporation*.

76

evaporate

[ee•VAP•uh•rayt]

To change from a liquid to a gas.

The sun's heat causes ocean water to *evaporate*.

75

© Harcourt

evidence

excretion

excretory system

experiment

excretion

[eks•KREE•shuhn]

The removal of wastes from the body.

Sweating is one kind of *excretion*.

78

evidence

[EV•uh•duhns]

Information, collected during an investigation, to support a hypothesis.

A scientist gathers *evidence* from an experiment.

77

experiment

[ek•SPAIR•uh•muhnt]

A procedure you carry out under controlled conditions to test a hypothesis.

Experiments are an important part of the scientific method.

80

excretory system

[EKS•kruh•tawr•ee SIS•tuhm]

The system that removes wastes from the body.

Cellular wastes leave the body through the *excretory system*.

79

© Harcourt

ferment

fermentation

flood basin

fog

© Harcourt

fermentation

[fer•muhn•TAY•shuhn]

The process that releases energy from sugar in the absence of oxygen.

Fermentation bubbles are what cause bread dough to rise.

82

ferment

[FUR•ment]

To release energy from sugar in the absence of oxygen.

Yeast *ferments* making bread dough rise.

81

fog

[FAWG]

A cloud that forms near the ground.

Fog can make it hard for drivers to see the road ahead.

84

flood basin

[FLUHD BAY•suhn]

An area of land that "catches" the runoff from urban areas in a human-made lake.

When people build near a *flood basin*, their houses are at risk of being flooded.

83

© Harcourt

force

forecast

formula

freeze

forecast

[FAWR•kast]

The prediction of future weather.

Meteorologists make weather *forecasts*.

force

[FAWRS]

A push or pull that causes an object to move, stop, or change direction.

Forces affect the movement of objects.

freeze

[FREEZ]

To change from a liquid to a solid.

Water *freezes* at 0°C (32°F).

formula

[FAWRM•yuh•luh]

Symbols that show how many atoms of each element are present.

The *formula* for water is H_2O.

freezing

front

full moon

fusion

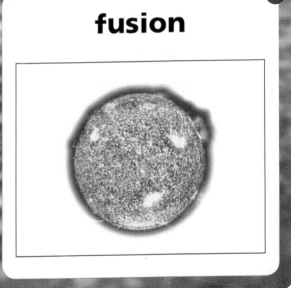

© Harcourt

front

[FRUHNT]

A place where two air masses meet.

Sometimes you can locate a *front* by watching the clouds.

90

freezing

[FREEZ•ing]

Having an air temperature below 0°C (32°F).

Dripping water can form icicles when the temperature outdoors is *freezing*.

89

fusion

[FYOO•zhuhn]

The energy–producing reaction that occurs inside of stars.

Fusion inside the sun produces solar energy.

92

full moon

[FUL MOON]

The moon phase in which all of the moons surface facing Earth is visible.

A second *full moon* in any month is called a blue moon.

91

gas 93

glacier 94

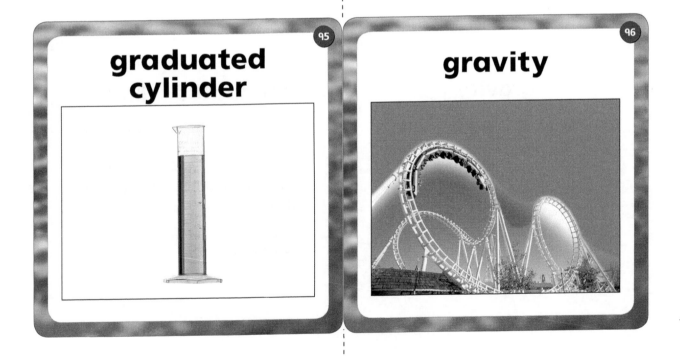

graduated cylinder 95

gravity 96

glacier

[GLAY•sher]

A huge sheet of moving ice.

Glaciers form in places where new snow falls faster than old snow melts.

gas

[GAS]

The state of matter that does not have a definite shape or volume.

These balloons contain helium *gas*.

gravity

[GRAV•ih•tee]

The force that pulls objects toward Earth.

On a roller coaster, you experience the effects of *gravity*.

graduated cylinder

[GRA•joo•ay•tuhd SIL•uhn•der]

A tool used to make quantitative observations of the volume of liquids.

Graduated cylinders come in several sizes.

© Harcourt

groundwater

hail

heart

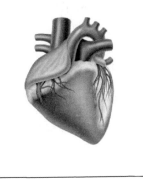

helium

hail

[HAYL]

Raindrops that freeze, are coated with more water, refreeze, and then fall as pieces of ice.

Hail sometimes falls in summer thunderstorms.

98

groundwater

[GROWND•wawt•er]

Water that is located in soil and rocks below Earth's surface.

You can pump *groundwater* from a well.

97

helium

[HEE•lee•uhm]

A gas that is the product of fusion inside of stars.

Helium is lighter than air, so it makes balloons float.

100

heart

[HART]

An organ that pumps blood throughout the body.

The muscle tissue in your *heart* is very strong.

99

© Harcourt

high pressure

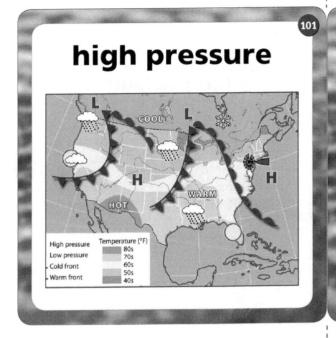

	Temperature (°F)
High pressure	80s
Low pressure	70s
Cold front	60s
Warm front	50s
	40s

101

humidity

102

hurricane

103

hydrogen

104

humidity

[hyoo•MID•uh•tee]

A measurement of the amount of water vapor in the air.

When the *humidity* is high, your sweat evaporates slowly.

102

high pressure

[HY•PRESH•er]

An area of dense, cold air.

Weather maps often show areas of *high pressure* with the letter "H".

101

hydrogen

[HY•druh•juhn]

A reactant of fusion inside of stars.

Fusion can change *hydrogen* to helium.

104

hurricane

[HER•ih•kayn]

A large, rotating tropical storm system with wind speeds of at least 119 km/hr (74 mi/hr).

Hurricanes form over warm ocean waters.

103

hydrologic cycle

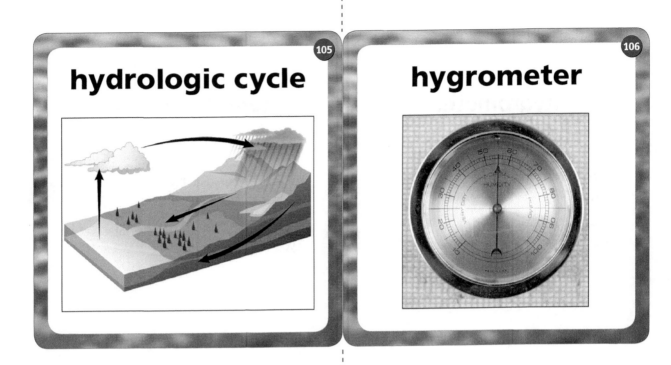

hygrometer

hypothesis

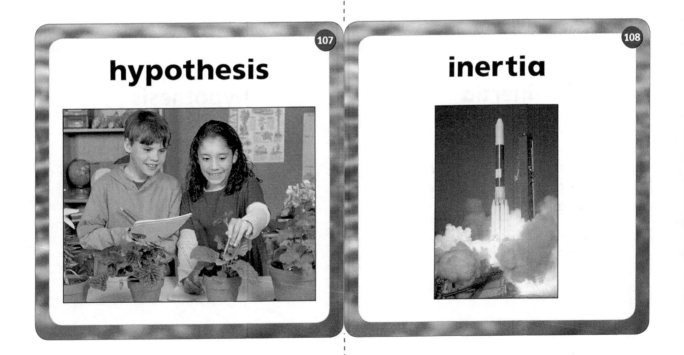

inertia

hygrometer

[hy•GRAHM•uht•er]

An instrument for measuring humidity.

A *hygrometer* shows the relative humidity.

hydrologic cycle

[hy•druh•LAHJ•ik SY•kuhl]

Another term for the water cycle.

The *hydrologic cycle* and the water cycle are the same thing.

inertia

[in•ER•shuh]

The property of matter that keeps an object at rest or moving in a straight line.

It takes more force to start something moving due to *inertia*.

hypothesis

[hy•PAHTH•uh•sis]

A statement that provides a testable possible answer to a scientific question.

These students are testing a *hypothesis* with their experiment.

inquiry

intestine

investigation

Jupiter

intestine

[in•TES•tuhn]

Two connected tubes, the small and large intestines, leading from the stomach that help the body absorb water and nutrients and help rid the body of waste.

Food moves from your stomach to your small *intestine*.

110

inquiry

[IN•kwer•ee]

An organized way to gather information and answer questions.

You must observe carefully in a scientific *inquiry*.

109

Jupiter

[JOO•pit•er]

The fifth planet from the sun and the largest planet in the solar system.

The Great Red Spot on *Jupiter* is a storm that has been going on for more than 300 years.

112

investigation

[in•ves•tuh•GAY•shuhn]

A procedure that is carried out to gather data about an object or event.

The student is conducting an *investigation* and recording the results.

111

© Harcourt

kidney

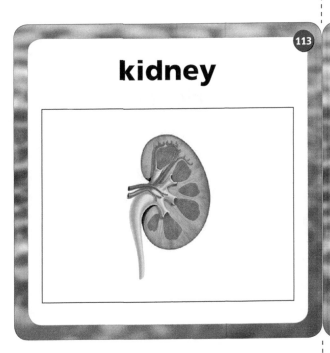

113

latitude

114

liquid

115

local wind

116

latitude

[LAT•uh•tood]

An area's distance from the equator.

Lines of *latitude* are parallel to the equator.

kidney

[KID•nee]

The main organ of the execretory system.

You have two *kidneys*.

local wind

[LOH•kuhl WIND]

Wind that results from local changes in temperature.

A land breeze is a *local wind* that blows from the land.

liquid

[LIK•wid]

The state of matter that has a definite volume but no definite shape.

Milk is one kind of *liquid*.

low pressure

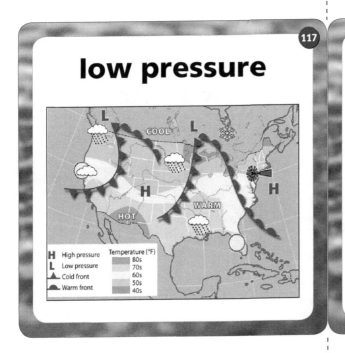

malleable

Mars

meniscus

© Harcourt

malleable

[MAL•ee•uh•buhl]

Easy to shape or to form.

Aluminum is a highly *malleable* metal.

118

low pressure

[LOH PRESH•er]

An area of warm, less dense air.

Stormy weather comes with a *low pressure* area, shown with a letter "L".

117

meniscus

[muh•NIS•kuhs]

The curved top of a column of liquid.

You can see the *meniscus* when you measure liquid in a graduated cylinder.

120

Mars

[MARZ]

The fourth planet from the sun.

Mars has the largest canyon in the solar system.

119

Mercury

121

metal

122

metal alloy

123

metallic

124

metal

[MET•uhl]

A substance that conducts heat and electricity well and is malleable.

Some structures are made of *metal*.

Mercury

[MER•kyur•ee]

The closest planet to the sun.

Mercury is a little bigger than Earth's moon.

metallic

[muh•TAL•ik]

Looking like metal.

Metallic objects are often shiny.

metal alloy

[MET•uhl AL•oy]

A solid solution in which a metal or nonmetal is dissolved in a metal.

Bronze is a *metal alloy* of copper and other materials.

metalloid

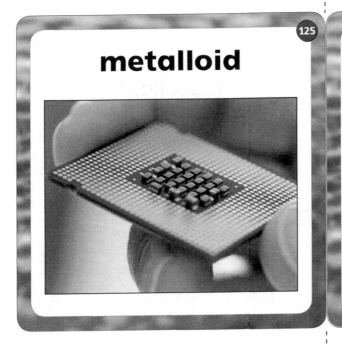

meteor

meteorite

meteorology

meteor

[MEET•ee•er]

A piece of rock that travels
through space.

Meteors are smaller than asteroids.

126

metalloid

[MET•uh•loyd]

A substance that has some of
the properties of a metal and
some of the properties of a
nonmetal.

This computer chip is made of silicon,
which is a *metalloid*.

125

meteorology

[meet•ee•uh•RAHL•uh•jee]

The study of weather.

Students use weather stations to help
them learn about *meteorology*.

128

meteorite

[MEET•ee•er•yt]

A meteor that reaches
Earth's surface.

Large *meteorites* can leave craters in
Earth's surface.

127

© Harcourt

methane

129

microscope

130

mixture

131

molecule

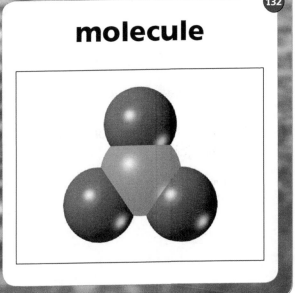

132

microscope

[MY•kruh•skohp]

A tool that makes small objects appear larger.

You can use a *microscope* to see things that you can't see with your eyes alone.

130

methane

[METH•ayn]

Natural gas containing carbon and hydrogen.

Gas stoves use *methane* to cook food.

129

molecule

[MAHL•ih•kyool]

A group of two or more atoms that are joined.

This *molecule* has two different kinds of atoms.

132

mixture

[MIKS•cher]

A combination of two or more different substances.

Fruit salad is a *mixture*.

131

monsoon

133

moon

134

mouth

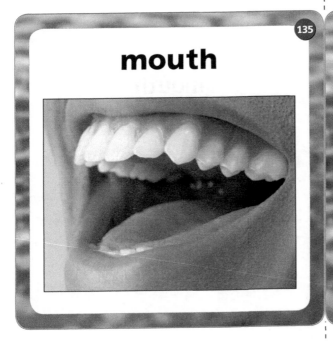

135

multicellular organism

136

moon

134

[MOON]

Any natural body that revolves around a planet.

Earth's *moon* causes ocean tides on Earth.

monsoon

133

[mahn•SOON]

A large wind system that reverses direction seasonally.

Monsoons often bring rain.

multicellular organisms

136

[mul•tih•SEL•yoo•ler AWR•guh•niz•uhm]

A living thing made up of many cells.

A snake is one kind of *multicellular organism*.

mouth

135

[MOWTH]

The opening through which an animal takes in food, beginning the process of digestion with certain foods.

Your *mouth* is part of your digestive system.

Neptune

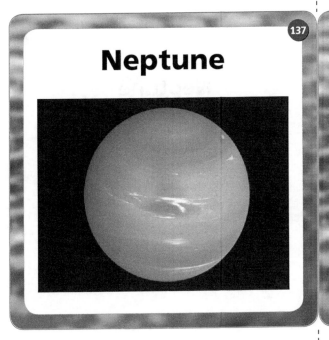

neutralize

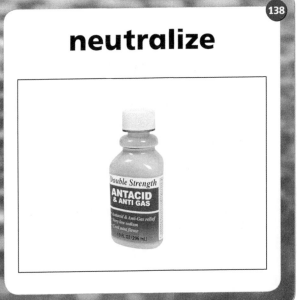

neutron

nitrogen

neutralize

[NOO•truh•lyz]

To make chemically neutral, as when an acid and a base are combined.

You can use a base to *neutralize* stomach acid.

138

Neptune

[NEP•toon]

The eighth planet from the sun.

Neptune's blue color is due to methane gas.

137

nitrogen

[NY•truh•juhn]

A nonmetal element.

Nitrogen is a gas that makes up most of Earth's atmosphere.

140

neutron

[NOO•trahn]

One of the particles in an atom.

Neutrons and protons are in the nucleus of an atom.

139

© Harcourt

noble gas

141

Neon

nonmetal

142

nonvascular plant

143

Northern Hemisphere

144

nonmetal

[nahn•MET•uhl]

A substance that does not conduct electricity and is not malleable.

Coal (carbon) is a *nonmetal,* because it does not conduct electricity and does not bend easily.

142

noble gas

[NOH•buhl GAS]

An element in the last column of the periodic table that doesn't combine with other elements.

Neon is a *noble gas.*

141

Northern Hemisphere

[NAWR•thern HEM•ih•sfir]

The half of Earth that is north of the equator, includes North America, Europe, Asia, and parts of Africa.

In the *Northern Hemisphere,* summer is in June, July, August, and September.

144

nonvascular plant

[NAHN•vas•kyuh•ler PLANT]

A plant without transport tubes to carry water and nutrients thoughout the plant.

Nonvascular plants don't grow very tall.

143

nucleus

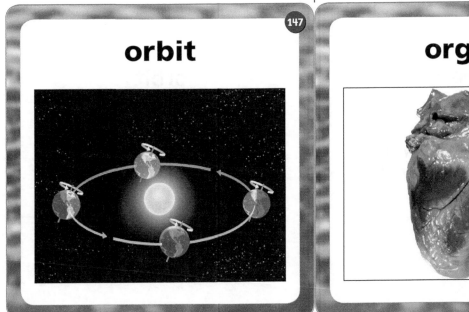

nucleus

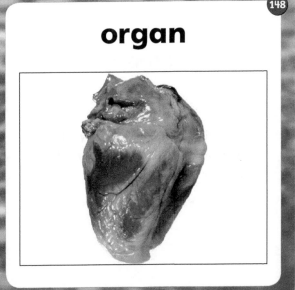

orbit

organ

© Harcourt

nucleus

[NOO•klee•uhs]

In a cell, the organelle that directs all of the cell's activities.

The *nucleus* controls how a cell works.

nucleus

[NOO•klee•uhs]

A dense area in the center of an atom, containing protons and neutrons.

All atoms have a *nucleus*.

organ

[AWR•guh]

A group of tissues that work together to perform a certain function.

The heart is one of your *organs*.

orbit

[AWR•bit]

The path that one body takes in space as it revolves around another body.

It takes 365.25 days for Earth to complete its *orbit* around the sun.

organ system

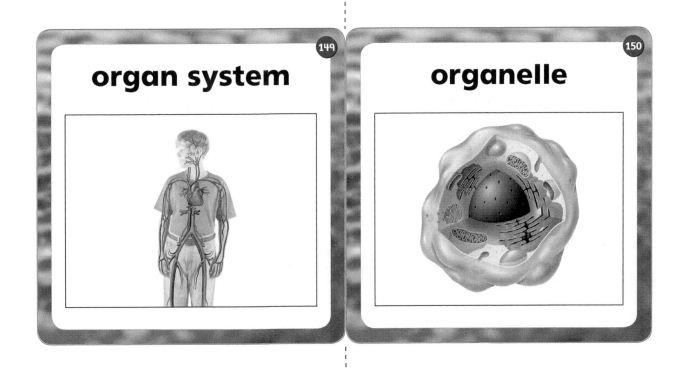

149

organelle

150

organism

151

oxygen

152

organelle

[AWR•guhn•NEL]

A structure in cells that has a specific function to help keep the cell alive.

A cell has many organelles.

150

organ system

[AWR•guhn SIS•tuhm]

A group of organs that work together to do a job for the body.

The digestive system is one kind of organ system.

149

oxygen

[AHK•sih•juhn]

A nonmetal element that reacts with many other elements.

Humans need oxygen gas to survive.

152

organism

[AWR•guh•niz•uhm]

A living thing.

Plants and animals are organisms.

151

periodic table

phase

phloem

photosynthesis

phase

[FAYZ]

One of the shapes the moon seems to have as it orbits Earth.

The moon waxes and wanes during its *phases*.

periodic table

[pir•ee•AHD•ik TAY•buhl]

A table that shows the elements arranged by their atomic numbers.

This *periodic table* shows more than 100 elements.

photosynthesis

[foht•oh•SIN•thuh•sis]

The process by which plants make food from carbon dioxide and water and release oxygen into the air.

Plants need light and water to perform *photosynthesis*.

phloem

[FLOH•em]

Vascular tissue that carries food from leaves to the other parts of a plant.

Phloem helps transport food throughout a plant.

physical change

157

physical property

158

physiology

159

planet

160

physical property

[FIZ•ih•kuhl PRAHP•er•tee]

A trait—such as color, shape, or hardness—that describes a substance by itself.

Some of the *physical properties* of this animal are its color and shape.

158

physical change

[FIZ•ih•kuhl CHAYNJ]

A change in which a substance remains the same substance.

Melting is one kind of *physical change*.

157

planet

[PLAN•it]

A body that revolves around a star.

Our solar system has nine *planets*.

160

physiology

[fiz•ee•AHL•uh•jee]

The study of how organisms function.

Understanding *physiology* can help runners win races.

159

planetary

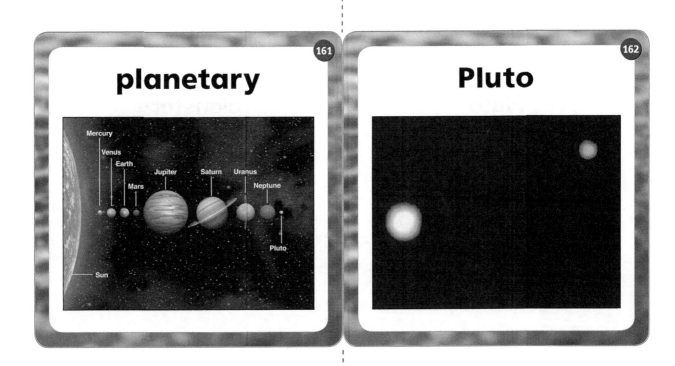

Pluto

pollution

precipitation

Pluto

[PLOOT•oh]

The ninth planet from the sun.

Pluto is smaller than Earth's moon.

162

planetary

[PLAN•uh•tair•ee]

Having to do with the planets.

Information about Mercury is one part of *planetary* science.

161

precipitation

[pree•sip•uh•TAY•shuhn]

Water that falls from clouds to the Earth.

Precipitation can be solid, like snow, or liquid, like rain.

164

pollution

[puh•LOOSH•uhn]

Any change to a resource that makes the resource unhealthy to use.

Factory smoke is a source of air *pollution*.

163

prevailing westerlies

165

prevailing wind

166

product

167

propane

168

prevailing wind

[pree•VAYL•ing wind]

A global wind that blows constantly from the same direction.

The picture shows Earth's *prevailing winds*.

166

prevailing westerlies

[pree•VAYL•ing

WES•ter•leez]

The prevailing winds over the United States that blow from the west.

The *prevailing westerlies* move weather systems from west to east.

165

propane

[PROH•payn]

Gas used in heating some homes and for cooking in outdoor barbeques.

This tank holds *propane* for the grill.

168

product

[PRAHD•uhkt]

A substance that is formed by a chemical reaction.

Carbon dioxide is one of the *products* of combining baking soda and vinegar.

167

© Harcourt

properties

proton

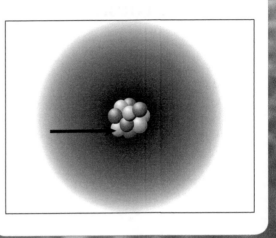

qualitative observation

quantitative observation

© Harcourt

proton

[PROH•tahn]

One of the particles in an atom.

Protons have a positive charge.

170

properties

[PRAHP•er•teez]

The physical and chemical qualities of a substance, such as size, texture or ability to react with other substances.

One of the *properties* of this glass jar is that it is smooth.

169

quantitative observation

[KWAHNT•uh•tayt•iv ahb•zer•VAY•shuhn]

An observation that involves numbers or measurements.

The student is using a balance to make a *quantitative observation*.

172

qualitative observation

[KWAWL•uh•tayt•iv ahb•zer•VAY•shuhn]

An observation that does not involve measurements or numbers.

A description of a smell is a *qualitative observation*.

171

quarter moon

173

rain

174

reactant

175

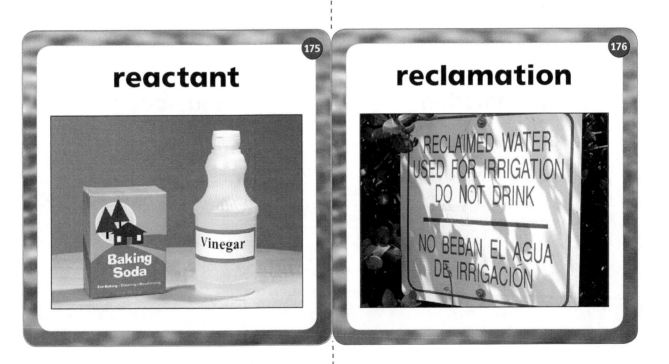

Baking Soda

For Baking • Cleaning • Deodorizing

Vinegar

reclamation

176

RECLAIMED WATER
USED FOR IRRIGATION
DO NOT DRINK

NO BEBAN EL AGUA
DE IRRIGACIÓN

rain

[RAYN]

Precipitation that is liquid water.

Some forest areas receive a lot of *rain*.

174

quarter moon

[KWAWRT•er MOON]

The moon phase half way between a new and a full moon.

A *quarter moon* looks like a semicircle.

173

reclamation

[rek•luh•MAY•shuhn]

The recycling of sewage water.

Sewage water can be used again if it goes through *reclamation*.

176

reactant

[ree•AK•tuhnt]

A substance that changes during a chemical reaction.

Vinegar and baking soda are *reactants* when you combine them.

175

recycle 177

recycling 178

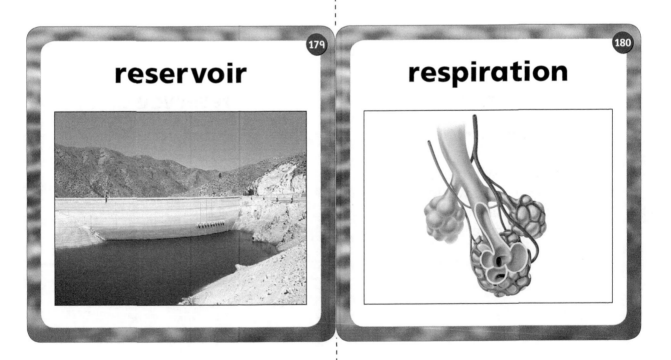

reservoir 179

respiration 180

recycling

[ree•SYK•ling]

Making new products from old ones.

Recycling is one way to help the environment.

recycle

[ree•SY•kuhl]

To use something again for a new purpose.

Trees *recycle* oxygen from carbon dioxide.

respiration

[res•puh•ray•shuhn]

The process in which oxygen is delivered to and waste products are taken away from the body's cells.

Alveoli are involved in *respiration.*

reservoir

[REZ•er•vwar]

A body of water stored for future use.

Reservoirs provide fresh water to many cities.

© Harcourt

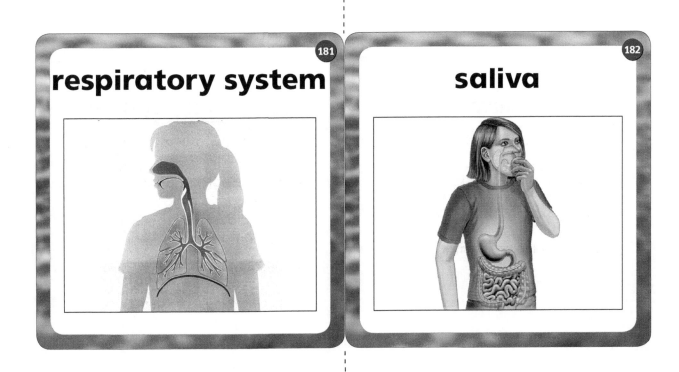

respiratory system
181

saliva
182

salt
183

satellite
184

saliva

[suh•LY•vuh]

A fluid produced by the mouth, that softens food, and begins the digestion of certain foods.

Saliva can help start digestion of starches.

182

respiratory system

[RES•per•uh•tawr•ee SIS•tuhm]

A group of organs and tissues that exchange oxygen and carbon dioxide between your body and the environment.

The *respiratory system* includes lungs.

181

satellite

[SAT•uh•lyt]

A body in space that orbits a larger body.

Some *satellites* are natural, and some are artificial.

184

salt

[SAWLT]

A substance that is made by combining an acid and a base.

The table salt you use on your food is just one kind of *salt*.

183

© Harcourt

Saturn

185

scientific method

186

sea level

187

seasonal

188

scientific method

[sy•uhn•TIF•ik METH•uhd]

A series of steps used to plan and carry out an experiment.

You can use the *scientific method* to answer your science questions.

186

Saturn

[SAT•ern]

The sixth planet from the sun.

Saturn has dozens of moons and many rings.

185

seasonal

[SEE•zuhn•uhl]

Dependent on or determined by the time of year.

Some trees show *seasonal* changes in the colors of their leaves.

188

sea level

[SEE LEV•uh]

The level of the surface of the ocean, used as a standard in measuring heights and depths.

Some areas of California are below *sea level*.

187

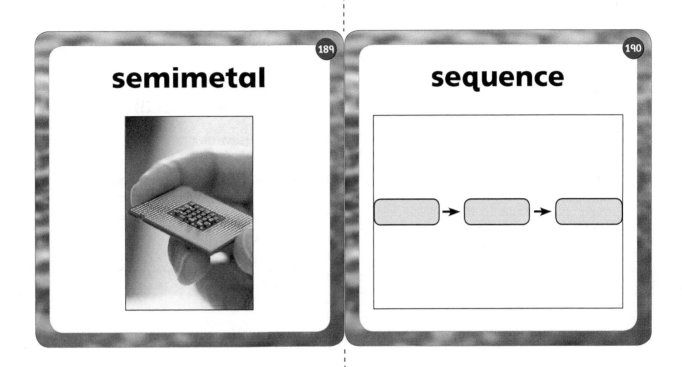

semimetal

sequence

severe weather

sleet

sequence

[SEE•kwuhns]

The order in which things happen.

Food moves through the digestive system in a certain sequence.

190

semimetal

[SEM•ee•met•uhl]

A substance that has some of the properties of a metal and some of the properties of a nonmetal.

This computer chip is made of silicon, which is a semimetal.

189

sleet

[SLEET]

Precipitation formed when rain passes through air that is cold enough to freeze water.

Sleet makes sidewalks very slippery.

192

severe weather

[suh•VIR WETH•er]

Extremely bad or dangerous weather, such as hurricanes, tornadoes, or thunderstorms.

It can be dangerous to be outside in severe weather.

191

snow

solar system

Mercury
Venus
Earth
Mars
Jupiter
Saturn
Uranus
Neptune
Pluto
Sun

solid

solubility

193

194

195

196

solar system

[SOH•ler SIS•tuhm]

A star and all the planets and other objects that revolve around it.

The largest planet in our *solar system* is Jupiter.

snow

[SNOH]

Precipitation that is formed when water vapor turns directly into ice crystals.

Flakes of *snow* are ice crystals.

solubility

[sahl•yu•BIL•uh•tee]

The ability to dissolve.

The drink mix has high *solubility*.

solid

[SAHL•id]

The state of matter that has a definite shape and a definite volume.

Sand is one example of a *solid*.

Southern Hemisphere

197

sphere

198

star

199

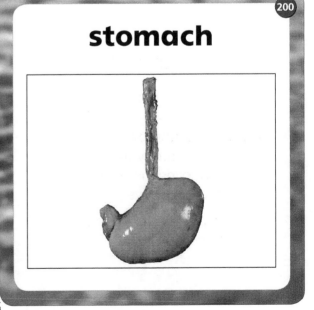

stomach

200

sphere

[SFIR]

The shape of planets and stars.

A sphere is the shape of a ball.

Southern Hemisphere

[SUHTH•ern HEM•ih•sfir]

The half of Earth south of the equator, includes South America, Australia, and much of Africa.

In the Southern Hemisphere, winter starts in June.

stomach

[STUHM•uhk]

A baglike organ of the digestive system with strong muscles that mixes food with digestive juices.

The stomach uses digestive juices to break down food.

star

[STAR]

A huge ball of very hot gases in space.

Stars look small from Earth's surface.

stomata

201

stratosphere

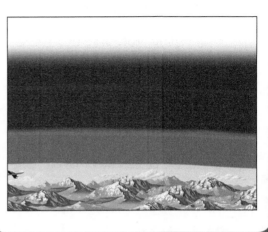

202

stratus

203

structure

204

© Harcourt

stratosphere

[STRAT•uh•sfir]

The layer of the atmoshpere containing ozone, and is above the troposphere.

Space shuttles must pass through the stratosphere on their way into orbit.

202

stomata

[STOH•muh•tuh]

On the underside of leaves, tiny holes that release waste products.

Some stomata can be seen only with a microscope.

201

structure

[STRUHK•cher]

In an organism, a part that can be recognized by its shape and other properties.

This bird's wing is a structure.

204

stratus

[STRAT•uhs]

A type of cloud that forms low in the atmosphere, possibly leading to light precipitation.

Stratus clouds may look as if they are closer to Earth's surface than other kinds of clouds.

203

sublimation

205

sun

206

teeth

207

telescope

208

sun

[SUHN]

The star at the center of the solar system.

The *sun* provides light and heat energy to our solar system.

sublimation

[suhb•luh•MAY•shuhn]

A change from a solid to a gas without becoming a liquid.

These ice crystals formed through *sublimation*.

telescope

[TEL•uh•skohp]

A tool that scientists use to study parts of the universe not visible to the human eye.

Powerful *telescopes* on Earth and in space reveal faraway parts of the universe.

teeth

[TEETH]

The hard structures in the mouth that grind food into smaller pieces.

People have two sets of *teeth* during their lives.

temperature

209

thermal conductivity

210

thunderstorm

211

tissue

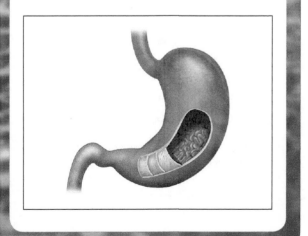

212

thermal conductivity

[THER•muhl kahn•duhk•TIV•uh•tee]

The ability of a metal to trans-fer thermal energy easily.

The wires inside the toaster have high *thermal conductivity.*

210

temperature

[TEM•per•uh•cher]

The measure of the quantity of heat in the atmosphere.

Thermometers are used to measure *temperature.*

209

tissue

[TISH•oo]

A group of cells that work together to perform a certain function.

The lining of the stomach is one kind of *tissue.*

212

thunderstorm

[THUHN•der•stawrm]

A storm with rain, lightning, hail, and thunder.

Thunderstorms happen in every part of the country.

211

tornado

213

trade wind

214

transpiration

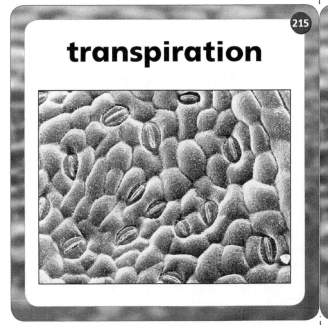

215

tropical storm

216

© Harcourt

trade wind

[TRAYD WIND]

A prevailing wind near the equator.

The movement of air near the equator causes *trade winds.*

tornado

[tawr•NAY•doh]

A violently spinning column of air that touches the ground.

The inside of a *tornado* has very low air pressure.

tropical storm

[TRAHP•ih•kuhl STAWRM]

A cyclone in which wind speeds are between 63-118 km/hr (39-73 mph).

Tropical storms are less severe than hurricanes.

transpiration

[tran•spuh•RAY•shuhn]

The process by which water moves up and out of plants through tiny holes in their leaves.

Plants recycle water through *transpiration.*

troposphere

Uranus

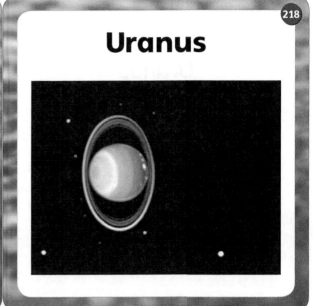

urine

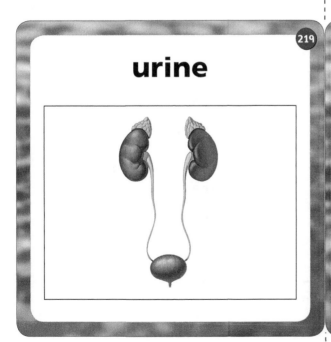

vacuole

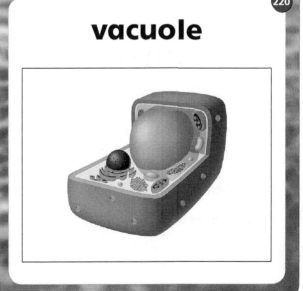

Uranus

[YUR•uh•nuhs]

The seventh planet in our solar system.

Uranus takes 84 Earth years to orbit the sun.

218

troposphere

[TROH•puh•sfir]

The layer of atmoshpere closest to Earth's surface.

Planes travel in the *troposphere*.

217

vacuole

[VAK•yoo•ohl]

A plant organelle that stores nutrients, water, and waste until the cell uses or gets rid of them.

Vacuoles are like storerooms for plant cells.

220

urine

[YUR•in]

A liquid waste product pro- duced by the body.

Urine is stored in the bladder.

219

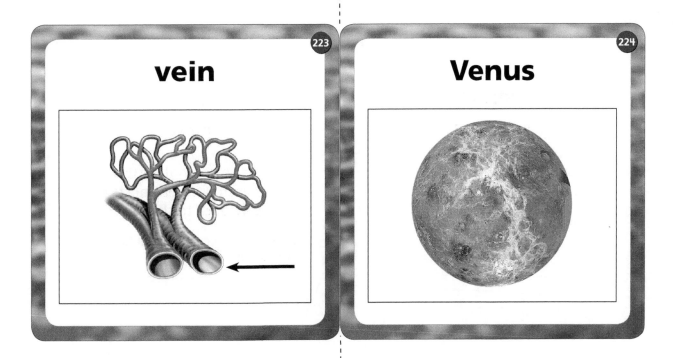

vascular plant 221

vascular tissue 222

vein 223

Venus 224

vascular tissue

[VAS•kyuh•ler TISH•oo]

Tissue that supports a plant and carries water and food throughout the plant.

You can find *vascular tissue* in tree trunks.

222

vascular plant

[VAS•kyuh•ler PLANT]

A plant with tubes to carry nutrients and water throughout the plant.

Trees are *vascular plants.*

221

Venus

[VEE•nuhs]

The second planet from the sun.

Venus is about the same size as Earth.

224

vein

[VAYN]

A blood vessel that carries blood from different parts of the body back to the heart.

Veins (blue) carry blood that has little oxygen.

223

© Harcourt

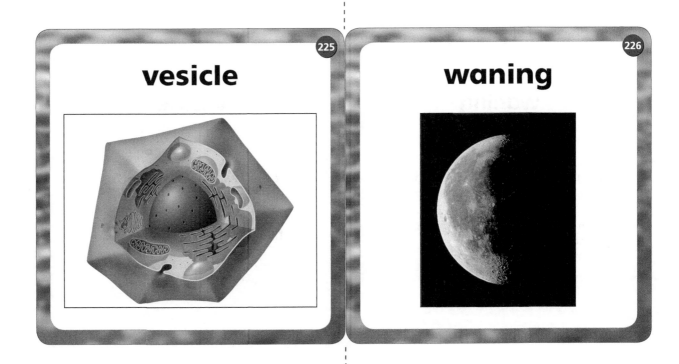

vesicle 225

waning 226

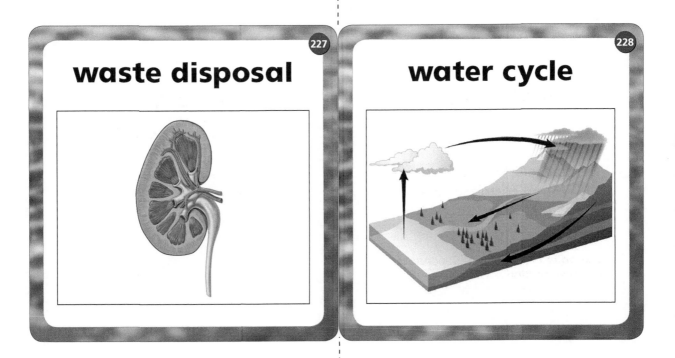

waste disposal 227

water cycle 228

waning

[WAYN•ing]

The process in which the moon goes from full to new.

When the moon is *waning*, the lighted part seen from Earth gets smaller each night.

vesicle

[VEHS•uh•kuhl]

An animal organelle that stores nutrients, water, and waste until the cell uses or gets rid of them.

Vesicles are like storerooms for animal cells.

water cycle

[WAWT•er SY•kuhl]

The constant movement of water from Earth's surface to Earth's atmosphere and back to Earth's surface.

The *water cycle* includes evaporation and precipitation.

waste disposal

[WAYST dis•POH•zuhl]

The removal of waste products from an organism.

Every living thing has some kind of *waste disposal*.

water quality

water table

water vapor

watershed

© Harcourt

water table

[WAWT•er TAY•buhl]

The top of groundwater.

Surface pollution can get down to the *water table* quickly.

water quality

[WAWT•er KWAWL•uh•tee]

The measure of how safe water is for human use.

The *water quality* in the city is tested regularly.

watershed

[WAWT•er•shed]

An area of land that is drained by a series of creeks and rivers.

Water quality is affected by all the pollution in a *watershed.*

water vapor

[WAWT•er VAY•per]

The gas form of water.

Water vapor is formed when water boils.

waxing

233

weather

234

weather front

235

wind

236

© Harcourt

weather

[WETH•er]

The condition of the atmosphere at a certain place
and time.

Weather can affect people's activities,
especially if it is severe.

234

waxing

[WAKS•ing]

The process in which the moon
goes from new to full.

When the moon is *waxing*, the lighted
part seen from Earth gets bigger each
night.

233

wind

[WIND]

The horizontal movement of air.

The *wind* is strong enough to bend
these young trees.

236

weather front

[WETH•er FRUHNT]

A place where two air masses
meet.

Weather fronts often change
the weather.

235

© Harcourt

wing

xylem

xylem

[ZY•luhm]

Vascular tissue that carries water and nutrients from roots to the other parts of the plant.

Xylem moves water from the roots up to the leaves.

(238)

wing

[WING]

One of the limbs that are typically used for flying by many animals, such as birds, bats, or insects.

A bat uses its *wings* to fly at night.

(237)

Writing Models

The writing models on the following pages show examples of writing for different purposes. Students can consult these models as they complete the Writing Links described in the *California Science* Student Edition or other writing assignments described in the Teacher Edition. You may wish to distribute copies of the writing models to students or display them on an overhead transparency.

Informative Writing

Persuasive Writing

Narrative Writing

Expressive Writing

Writing in Science

Model: How-To Writing

How-to writing gives directions or explains how to do something. Steps are given in time order.

topic sentence

materials needed

time-order words in steps

How to Grow a Plant

It's easy to grow a plant from a seed. To get started, you'll need a small plant pot and tray, a bag of potting soil, one or two large seeds, and a container of water.

First, place the tray under the pot. Then, carefully fill the pot with soil. Pat the soil down lightly to make it firm. Use your finger to poke a hole about $\frac{1}{2}$ inch deep in the soil. Next, put the seed in the hole. Cover the seed with soil. Then, water the soil until it is moist but not muddy. Set the pot near a sunny window. Water the soil every few days. In a few days, you will see a green shoot coming out of the soil. That means that the seed has germinated. Your plant will begin to grow. Water the little plant every day to keep the soil moist.

Writing in Science

Model: Classification

In a **classification essay,** a writer shows how things can be grouped into categories. Often, examples of each category are provided.

title	**Different Types of Resources**
topic sentence	Natural resources can be divided into three categories: nonrenewable, renewable, and reusable resources.
first category defined	Nonrenewable resources cannot be replaced in one lifetime after they are used up. Rock and mineral resources, such as coal, silicon, copper, and iron are nonrenewable resources. Oil is another nonrenewable resource.
second category defined	Renewable resources are resources that can be replaced as they are used. Forests are an example of a renewable resource. When full-grown trees are cut down to make paper and lumber, new trees can be planted to replace them.
third category defined	Reusable resources can be used over and over again. Air and water are good examples of reusable resources. It is important to remember that these resources are only reusable if people are careful. If air and water get polluted, they can become unusable.

Writing in Science

Model: Research Report

A **research report** provides information about a topic. Reports can be short, or they can be several pages long.

title	**The Galveston Hurricane**
introduction that identifies topic	The worst natural disaster in United States history was the Galveston, Texas hurricane of 1900. It helped people realize the importance of being prepared for storms.
body with detailed information about topic	The hurricane struck Galveston, a low coastal island, on September 8. Forecasters warned that severe weather was coming, but many people ignored or did not hear the warnings. Winds rose to an estimated 120 miles per hour. Huge waves swept over the city. Some survivors drifted for hours on pieces of lumber from shattered buildings. Others were not so lucky. By the time the storm ended, more than 8,000 people had lost their lives.
conclusion	The hurricane proved how important it is to be prepared for storms. After the hurricane, the citizens of Galveston built a sea wall to prevent future disasters. Meteorologists worked harder than ever to predict hurricanes and warn people about them.

Writing in Science

Model: Narration

A **narration** presents events in the order in which they occurred. Often, a narration is an eyewitness account of those events.

title	**Sunlight and Plant Growth**
introduction	Any science book will tell you that plants need sunlight to grow. Our science discovery team thinks that seeing is believing. That's why we did an experiment to show how sunlight affects plant growth.
topic sentence	
events described in time order	The first thing we did was to choose three pea plants. Each plant was 3 cm high. Plant "A" was placed by a window. In that spot, it would receive more than six hours of sunlight each day. Plant "B" was placed by the window for three hours each day. After that, it was placed in a covered box for the rest of the day. Plant "C" was kept in a covered box all day. Each plant was given 250 mL of water every three days.
conclusion	We followed this plan for two weeks. After that, the plants were measured again. Plant "A" had grown 12 cm. Plant "B" had grown 5 cm. Plant "C" had grown less than 2 cm. Our results were clear. Sunlight helps plants grow.

Writing in Science

Model: Explanation

In an **explanation,** the writer helps the reader understand something, such as what something is, how it works, what happens during a process, or why something happens.

title	## How Water Changes State
topic sentence	Water can be in any one of the three states of matter. It can be a solid, a liquid, or a gas. When heat is added or removed, water can change state.
body/detailed explanation	At temperatures at or below 0°C, water is in its solid state. The particles that make it up are packed closely together and move very little. Solid water, or ice, has a definite volume and shape.
	When solid water is heated to above 0°C, it changes to its liquid state. In liquid water, the particles move easily enough to slide past each other. When liquid water is cooled to 0°C, it changes back to its solid state.
	When water is heated to 100°C, it boils and changes to a gas called water vapor. The particles in the water vapor are far apart and move fast. When water vapor is cooled, it condenses, or turns to liquid.

Writing in Science

Model: Compare/Contrast

In a **compare-and-contrast essay,** a writer shows how two people, places, or things are alike and how they are different.

title	**Deer and Whales**
topic sentence	It may not seem like it at first, but the white-tailed deer and the blue whale are alike in many ways. Both animals are warm-blooded. Both animals keep their young close by when they are small. Both the deer and the blue whale breath air into their lungs. Both animals must forage for food to survive.
likenesses	
topic sentence	Even though they are both mammals, the white-tailed deer and the blue whale are very different. The deer is a land animal. It walks on four legs and eats plants such as grasses, twigs, and leaves. The whale is a water animal. It swims using its powerful flippers and tail. It feeds on tiny shrimp-like sea creatures called krill. The deer usually stays within a small territory. The blue whale may travel thousands of miles as it migrates each year.
differences	

Writing in Science

Model: Description

A **description** creates a word picture as it tells about one subject. It has a beginning, a middle, and an ending. It includes sensory details.

title	**The Avalanche**
beginning that tells what you will describe	The snow-covered mountains looked like a peaceful postcard. But in a matter of seconds, the beautiful scene changed to a picture of terror.
middle with sensory details	With a boom that echoed through the valley, a wall of snow began to tumble down the mountain. In an instant, the potential energy in the snow was transformed into kinetic energy. The avalanche quickly grew larger as it roared down the mountain's rocky face. Trees, boulders, and even buildings disappeared under the gigantic wave of snow.
ending	In less than two minutes, the avalanche was over. The energy of the avalanche was lost, as sound and as heat from the friction of the moving snow. Then all was still.

Writing in Science

Model: Opinion

An **opinion** essay has a beginning, a middle with paragraphs supporting the writer's opinion, and an ending.

title

beginning with opinion stated

middle with reasons to support opinion

ending with restated opinion or request for action

Protect Animal Habitats

Many threatened and endangered species are fighting to avoid extinction. I think the best way to protect them is to protect their habitats from damage by humans.

Human damage to animal habitats puts many species in danger. Each year, humans destroy millions of acres of wild lands to build new roads, homes, and businesses. This takes away the land where animals used to live. In addition, humans often pollute natural habitats. This makes them unfit for use by plants and animals. Humans also damage habitats by bringing in new species that prove harmful to animal populations that are already there.

If we are more careful about the way we use land, we will do less damage to habitats. With healthy habitats to live in, endangered and threatened species will be able to survive.

Writing in Science

Model: Request

To **request** information or products from a company, use a business-letter format. A business letter has the same parts as a friendly letter, plus an inside address. It also uses formal language.

heading

15 Main Street
Worcester, VT 05682
July 15, 2001

inside address

Mr. Jacob Lee
313 Hollis Street
Montpelier, VT 05602

greeting

Dear Mr. Lee:

statement of request and supporting reasons

The Worcester Mountain Club will be taking its annual endangered plant survey on September 3. I would like to invite you to help in this effort.

Before we can protect the endangered plants in the Worcester Range, we must identify them. We cannot do this without the help of volunteers.

Over the years, people from across Vermont have helped us with our survey. Their hard work has paid off. Last Labor Day, we discovered three species never before seen in the Worcester Range.

We look forward to another fun survey day this September 3. Won't you please join us? We will meet at the Worcester Mountain House, 15 Elmore Road, at 9 A.M.

closing

Sincerely,

signature

Suzanne Hollister

Writing in Science

Model: Business Letter

In a **business letter,** a writer uses formal language to ask for or share information, to request something, or to praise or complain about a product or service. It has the same parts as a friendly letter, plus an inside address.

heading	9 Bennett St. Eldred, PA 16731 September 15, 2002
inside address	Ms. Eleanor Nucci Corning Museum of Glass One Museum Way Corning, NY 14830
greeting	Dear Ms. Nucci:
	Our fifth-grade class at Eldred Elementary School would like to thank you for the personal tour of the Corning Museum of Glass. We really appreciate that you took the time to answer all of our questions. We all learned a lot about how glass is made and used.
body	Since returning to our school, we have begun to research how glass is used in the computer industry. And we have also begun a glass recycling program at our school. We thought you would be glad to hear that!
	Thank you again for your informative tour.
closing	Sincerely,
signature	James Paige

Writing in Science

Model: Story

Every **story** has a setting (time and place), one or more characters, and a series of events, called a plot. A plot has a beginning, a middle, and an end.

title

beginning: introduce the setting and the characters

middle: a plot with a problem to solve

end: the problem is solved

The Discovery

Dr. Andrea Shaughnessey began her day as she usually did. She put on her oxygen tank and mask, so she could breathe outdoors without choking on the black, polluted air.

As she walked to her laboratory, she wondered how the pollution had gotten so bad. If only people had listened to the warnings. But now it was too late—unless her experiment was a success. She had worked for ten years to build a machine that filtered pollutants from the atmosphere. The results of the test run would arrive this morning.

"Wouldn't it be great," she thought, "if people could stop to smell the roses again? Well, first we'd have to grow some roses since they haven't been able to survive with so little sunlight. But then, people could stop to smell them!"

When Andrea reached the lab, she didn't have to guess the test results. The other scientists on her team welcomed her with a cheer! The results had received an e-mail from the space agency that morning. The machine worked even better than they had hoped. Everyone could breath a sigh of relief. Andrea was a hero!

© Harcourt

Writing in Science

Model: Personal Story

A **personal story** is told in the first person. Someone or something is telling the story, using pronouns such as *I, my,* and *me.* Like any story, there is a beginning, a middle, and an end.

title	**Wetlands Surprise**
beginning: the narrator is identified	When my father told me we would visit the Callard Creek Wetland, I wasn't too excited. To me, a wetland was nothing more than a boring old swamp. "You're in for a surprise," Dad said, but I didn't believe him. Was I ever wrong!
middle: the narrator tells a series of events	By the time the sun rose, we had paddled our canoe half a mile out into the wetland. Suddenly, the world around us exploded with life. Flocks of snow geese spread their wings and took flight. Tall, regal herons fished along the edges of the weed beds. Muskrats and turtles swam so close to our canoe, I could almost touch them. The whole day was filled with incredible sights and sounds.
end: the narrator wraps up the story	On the way home, Dad asked me if I had been too bored by the "old swamp." I just smiled, knowing I would return to Callard Creek again and again.

Writing in Science

Model: Poem

A **poem** uses rhythm and language that appeals to the senses to paint a "word picture" for the reader. Some poems have rhyming lines, but some poems do not.

title	**Hibernation**
"word pictures" that help the reader picture what the poem is about	My body has stored its winter fat.
	Even the sun is cold.
	The geese have flown.
	The night has painted
	Sheets of ice upon the rivers.
	It is time for the long sleep.

Writing in Science

Model: Friendly Letter

In a **friendly letter,** a person writes to someone he or she knows. A friendly letter has a heading, a greeting, a body, a closing, and a signature. In the heading, include a comma between the city and state, and between the day of the month and the year.

heading (writer's address and date)

2214 Westgate Drive
St. Paul, MN 55114
August 10, 2001

greeting

Dear Andrew,

I hope you are having fun since you got back from space camp. It was cool to learn about the space stations and the different kinds of space probes. I loved building our own rocket, too. Even though our rocket didn't go the highest, I think it was the best. We made an excellent engineering team.

body

Have you gotten your new telescope yet? Mom and Dad say I can have one, but I have to earn some of the money myself. I guess that means I'll be starting out with something a little smaller than the Hubble telescope we learned about!

When we both get our telescopes, maybe you can come and visit me for a night of star gazing. Until then, keep your eye on the sky. Write me back when you have any news.

closing

Your friend,

signature

Luis

Rubrics for Writing Practice

A Six-Point Scoring Scale

Student work produced for writing assessment can be scored by using a six-point scale. Although each rubric includes specific descriptors for each point score, each score can also be framed in a more global perspective.

SCORE OF 6: EXEMPLARY. Writing at this level is both exceptional and memorable. It is often characterized by distinctive and unusually sophisticated thought processes, rich details, and outstanding craftsmanship.

SCORE OF 5: STRONG. Writing at this level exceeds the standard. It is thorough and complex, and it consistently portrays exceptional control of content and skills.

SCORE OF 4: PROFICIENT. Writing at this level meets the standard. It is solid work that has more strengths than weaknesses. The writing demonstrates mastery of skills and reflects considerable care and commitment.

SCORE OF 3: DEVELOPING. Writing at this level shows basic, although sometimes inconsistent, mastery and application of content and skills. It shows some strengths but tends to have more weaknesses overall.

SCORE OF 2: EMERGING. Writing at this level is often superficial, fragmented, or incomplete. It may show a partial mastery of content and skills, but it needs considerable development before reflecting the proficient level of performance.

SCORE OF I: BEGINNING. Writing at this level is minimal. It typically lacks understanding and use of appropriate skills and strategies. The writing may contain major errors.

Student _____ Date _____

Evaluator _____

Rubric for Ideas/Content

Score	Description
6	The writing is exceptionally clear, focused, and interesting. It holds the reader's attention throughout. Main ideas stand out and are developed by strong support and rich details suitable to the audience and the purpose.
5	The writing is clear, focused, and interesting. It holds the reader's attention. Main ideas stand out and are developed by supporting details suitable to the audience and the purpose.
4	The writing is clear and focused. The reader can easily understand the main ideas. Support is present, although it may be limited or rather general.
3	The reader can understand the main ideas, although they may be overly broad or simplistic, and the results may not be effective. Supporting details are often limited, insubstantial, overly general, or occasionally slightly off topic.
2	The main ideas and purpose are somewhat unclear, or development is attempted but minimal.
1	The writing lacks a central idea or purpose.

Rubric for Organization

Score	Description
6	The organization enhances the central idea(s) and its development. The order and structure are compelling and move the reader through the text easily.
5	The organization enhances the central idea(s) and its development. The order and structure are strong and move the reader through the text.
4	The organization is clear and coherent. Order and structure are present but may seem formulaic.
3	An attempt has been made to organize the writing; however, the overall structure is inconsistent or skeletal.
2	The writing lacks a clear organizational structure. An occasional organizational device is discernible; however, either the writing is difficult to follow and the reader has to reread substantial portions, or the piece is simply too short to demonstrate organizational skills.
1	The writing lacks coherence; organization seems haphazard and disjointed. Even after rereading, the reader remains confused.

Rubric for Sentence Fluency

Score	Description
6	The writing has an effective flow and rhythm. Sentences show a high degree of craftsmanship, with consistently strong and varied structure that makes expressive oral reading easy and enjoyable.
5	The writing has an easy flow and rhythm. Sentences are carefully crafted, with strong and varied structure that makes expressive oral reading easy and enjoyable.
4	The writing flows; however, connections between phrases or sentences may be less than fluid. Sentence patterns are somewhat varied, contributing to ease in oral reading.
3	The writing tends to be mechanical rather than fluid. Occasional awkward constructions may force the reader to slow down or reread.
2	The writing tends to be either choppy or rambling. Awkward constructions often force the reader to slow down or reread.
1	The writing is difficult to follow or to read aloud. Sentences tend to be incomplete, rambling, or very awkward.

Rubric for Word Choice

Score	Description
6	The words convey the intended message in an exceptionally interesting, precise, and natural way appropriate to the audience and the purpose. The writer employs a rich, broad range of words that have been carefully chosen and thoughtfully placed for impact.
5	The words convey the intended message in an interesting, precise, and natural way appropriate to the audience and the purpose. The writer employs a broad range of words that have been carefully chosen and thoughtfully placed for impact.
4	The words effectively convey the intended message. The writer employs a variety of words that are functional and appropriate to the audience and the purpose.
3	The language is quite ordinary, lacking interest, precision, and variety, or may be inappropriate to the audience and the purpose in places. The writer does not employ a variety of words, producing a sort of "generic" paper filled with familiar words and phrases.
2	The language is monotonous and/or misused, detracting from the meaning and impact.
1	The writing shows an extremely limited vocabulary or is so filled with misuses of words that the meaning is obscured. Because of vague or imprecise language, only the most general kind of message is communicated.